2⁵⁰

RIDDING YOURSELF

OF PSYCHOSOMATIC

HEALTH-WRECKERS

RIDDING YOURSELF

OF PSYCHOSOMATIC

HEALTH-WRECKERS

Alfred J. Cantor, M.D.

Editor-in-Chief, *American Journal of Proctology*; Founding
President, The International Academy of Proctology; Founder
and President Emeritus, Academy of Psychosomatic Medicine;
Founder, American College of Proctology; Regent and Secretary, The International Board of Proctology; Founder-Diplo-
mate, The International Board of Applied Nutrition; Author:
*Painless Rectal Surgery, Ambulatory Proctology, A Handbook
of Psychosomatic Medicine, Cancer Can Be Cured, Control of
Constipation, How to Lose Weight the Doctor's Way, Unitrol,*
and numerous other works

West Nyack
N. Y.

PARKER
PUBLISHING
COMPANY, INC.

PRINTED IN THE UNITED STATES OF AMERICA
78111—B & P

Dedicated to the eternal search for better
health and longer life and to the healing
magic of the mind as taught by UNITROL

prepared under the auspices of
the UNITROL Teaching Institute
147-41 Sanford Ave.
Flushing, N. Y.

Acknowledgements . . .

As with each of my books, I find myself ever grateful to my wife Eleanor and my children Pam and Jay for their understanding and their help in research, proofreading, typing, and evaluation.

My special gratitude is reserved for the many patients who have helped me as much as I have helped them. In this I must include the students of the UNITROL Teaching Institute in all parts of the world, whose studies and correspondence have enriched my life and experience while reconstructing theirs.

CONTENTS

RIDDING YOURSELF

OF PSYCHOSOMATIC

HEALTH-WRECKERS

HOW YOU WILL BENEFIT
FROM THIS BOOK

Patient—Heal Thyself!

Can you really heal yourself? The answer is generally a simple *yes*. Since over 90 per cent of all patients who visit the physician's office would probably get well even without treatment, it is obvious that the body does have the capacity to heal itself in most cases. The best physician is the one who makes an accurate diagnosis and then provides the patient with the necessary advice and medication to allow the body's natural recuperative powers the best opportunity to function on their own.

In other words, the best physician is the one who interferes the least. This is merely another way of saying that the patient not only can, but really *must,* heal himself. Obviously, however, he cannot heal himself if he has cancer, although there have been some reports of spontaneous cures of cancer. He cannot heal himself if he has an intestinal obstruction or a perforated peptic ulcer. There is no way for the body to melt away a brain tumor. And so we come to the recognition of strictly organic versus psychosomatic problems.

In this book you will learn to recognize psychosomatic problems. *You will learn that practically all disease is psychosomatic,* if the term is properly interpreted.

You will learn the distinction between the words *functional* and *organic,* and you will come to realize that the two cannot really be separated in the living organism. You will learn about the human functional unit, the integrated mind-body concept.

You will learn how to recognize your emotional problems and how to treat them.

The mysteries of personality development will be revealed

to you from infancy through adolescence and into mature, adult life.

After you have read the first few chapters of this book, you will know how to detect the psychosomatic health-wreckers, and how they arose in the first place. You will learn how to come to grips with and how to defeat these health-wreckers.

This book will tell you how to treat your anxiety problems— methods you can start using right now, in your own home. We will describe the now famous "Conflict Check Chart," and you will put it to immediate use. You will learn how to release your inhibited and repressed emotional dynamite to revitalize your mind and body.

You will learn the truth about tranquilizers. You will learn how to apply conditioning therapy—with and without self-hypnosis. You will learn about short-term psychotherapy and the famous Guided Association technique—a method that may save you years on the analyst's couch.

The mysteries of "Relaxation Therapy" will be revealed. You will not only learn *why* you should relax, but you will be taught *how* to relax, by several simple, basic methods.

You will then be introduced into the mysteries of *organ language*. You will learn how to recognize what your body is trying to tell you. Every organ-system will be described—and whether your problem is your intestinal tract, your heart or blood vessels, a matter of obesity, metabolism and your endocrine glands, your bones and joints, allergy, your sex organs, your nervous system, your lungs, your eyes or ears, or an acute anxiety, you will understand whatever your body is trying to tell you. In other words, *you will understand the body's organ language*.

Revealing case histories will show how other sufferers learned to control and correct their problems—problems very much like your own. Each chapter will tell you, in a simple, step-by-step fashion, how to use the method or combination of methods best suited for control of your anxiety and pain. You will learn how to get rid of the symptoms of your psychosomatic health-wreckers.

This book will teach you how to recognize and cope with:
- Emotional problems
- Anxiety states
- Headaches
- Back pains
- Your problem when you "don't feel well but don't know what to do about it."
- Gland failure
- Low blood-sugar weakness
- Arthritis
- The anxious, worried heart
- Low blood pressure
- High blood pressure
- Coronary heart disease (the painful heart attack)
- The worried stomach
- Stomach ulcer
- Nervous indigestion
- Nervous vomiting
- The ball-in-the-throat, "I can't swallow that" feeling
- The worried large bowel
- Constipation
- Diarrhea (the worried, loose bowel)
- Excess bowel secretion
- The infected, bleeding bowel
- Piles
- Skin problems like acne, itching, etc.
- Allergy
    hay fever
    asthma
    frequent colds
    hives
- Severe migraine headaches
- Insomnia (how to overcome sleepless nights)
- Dizziness
- Fainting
- Weakness
- Epileptic fits

- Poor eyesight
- Night blindness
- Hardened eyeballs (glaucoma)
- Your cihldren's feeding and toilet training problems and thumb sucking
- Special female or male problems
    painful monthly periods
    change of life, etc.
- Obesity

    Excess weight is a major psychosomatic health-wrecker, killing millions each year. This book gives you simple methods for control of this psychosomatic killer without drugs.

You will find important Symptom Lists at the beginning of Chapters 6 through 15. They tell you how to use this book and the special chapters describing your own type of symptoms. These "how to use this chapter" pages are your step-by-step guide to the simple, one-two-three methods of getting rid of psychosomatic health-wreckers.

You are now ready to start your adventure on the life-giving path to better health.

HOW TO USE THIS BOOK

This is a very special book—practical, realistic, down to earth —ready for you to put to use at once. You will find step-by-step methods—*methods you can use in your own home* for the relief of your pyschosomatic problems.

This Is What You Do—

1. First glance through the book, the table of contents and the chapter headings, to find the conditions *you* want to correct.

Check the Symptom Lists at the beginning of Chapters 6 through 15. These are especially important, for they tell you how to use each chapter and the entire book to help you rid yourself of your psychosomatic health-wreckers.

For example, let us suppose that your symptoms appear to be those of a heart condition. Chapter 7 is for you; turn to it at once. If you have stomach trouble, turn to Chapter 6. Headaches? Turn to Chapter 14.

2. Now read through the chapter you have selected, the one dealing with *your* problem.

3. You will find case histories similar to your own, and you will see how others conquered their problems. These everyday problem cases, with psychosomatic symptoms very much like your own, show you to how to use the amazing self-treatment methods of the CONFLICT CHECK CHART, Guided Association, Instant Relaxation and Instant Pain Release, and others, as practical keys to self-help.

4. You will also learn how to lengthen your life and how to strengthen all your other vital organs at the same time.

5. Now, here is the most important feature of this book— *turn back to Chapter 4* and fill out the amazing CONFLICT CHECK CHART. Do this at once, right now if you wish, and you will discover the major areas of anxiety in your life. Worry is the key to

psychosomatic disorders and disease. When you have located your hidden emotional dynamite, you can then proceed to the next step.

6. Now—turn to Chapter 5 and use the information you have just uncovered by means of the CONFLICT CHECK CHART to get rid of this emotional, symptom-causing, anxiety-laden dynamite.

How do you accomplish this remarkable and essential release from nervous tension? Chapter 5 reveals the rapid method you can use *right now* and *in your own home*—Guided Association, the author's original and world-famous self-treatment that gives you a sense of release. Using this method, you attain freedom from fear and tension and a completely revitalized capacity to handle all your anxiety problems, including those of the anxious heart, the troubled stomach, the aching head, the burdened back, and similar disorders.

Guided Association only takes a few minutes of your time each day, and may accomplish for you the same results that otherwise take years of treatment on an analyst's couch. Your symptoms may rapidly come under control, and may soon disappear. And best of all—*you do it yourself*—at home, in the privacy of your own room.

7. Now you will learn how to switch off your brain and how to practice Self-Suggestion more intelligently.

You will learn KEY WORD magic for Instant Action—such as Instant Sleep, Instant Pain Release, etc.

8. Now that you have started to put this book to use in the relief and control of your emotionally-based health problems, your psychosomatic health-wreckers, you will turn back to the previous section of this practical book for a quick summary of the difference between Organic and Functional disease, and the real meaning of the word *psychosomatic*. This will help you to straighten out your thinking on what is and what isn't psychosomatic. You will be surprised to find out that no matter what your condition is, the methods in this book will help you and your doctor.

9. Now you are at last ready to put your practical knowledge to full use, not only for your present symptoms, but also for the

prevention of troubles in the future. You will do this by reading through the entire book, and by using the methods you will learn —every day of your life.

Start with Chapter 1 and learn how to recognize the health-wreckers in your life.

Go on with Chapter 2, and you will be amazed at how your personality influences your health.

Then, in Chapter 3, you will be told about *organ language,* the code by which your body expresses feelings and thoughts that cannot be brought to your attention in any other way.

Re-read Chapters 4 and 5. This is the heart of the treatment method, and shows you exactly what to do—step-by-step—to get rid of your psychosomatic health-wreckers.

10. And now you will go to Chapter 16 and learn how to breathe for better health and longer life. You will learn how to combine the *Complete Breath* with *Continuous Affirmation* as a basic method for better thinking and living.

11. In short, you are now ready to read, to understand, and to *use* all parts of this book, from cover to cover, for complete Self-Mastery and for release from your psychosomatic health-wreckers.

And what else will this book do for you?

Most of us are overweight and aging more rapidly than Nature intended. If this is your problem, you need only turn to Chapter 8, and you will learn the simple and practical methods you can use, *without drugs,* to get rid of unsightly fat.

No matter what your psychosomatic problem is, you will find the answer as practical advice in the appropriate chapter.

This means that this book will not only help you get rid of your psychosomatic health-wreckers today, but will also be a *permanent* reference work for you as a guide to prevention and treatment in the future. It is a book designed to be used *throughout your lifetime*—every day.

Please look upon me as your guide in this adventure in better health and longer life. Take my hand in yours, and we will move step-by-step through the simple, practical methods to help you get rid of your psychosomatic health-wreckers.

The journey of a thousand miles begins with but a single step. We will now take that first step together.

Chapter 1

HOW TO RECOGNIZE
THE HEALTH-WRECKERS IN YOUR LIFE

Is your problem psychosomatic?

In this Chapter I will tell you the true meaning of the word *psychosomatic.* You will learn that practically all disease is psychosomatic, and that's a shocker when you stop to think about it. You will learn how to recognize psychosomatic problems. This is very easy, we must say, since almost all health problems are psychosomatic.

And you will come to realize that the words *functional* and *organic* are confusing, since all disease is both functional and organic. You will find out about the *magic hyphen,* and how to use it to get rid of much confusion in the use of words. And most important of all, you will come to realize that *getting rid of such confusion is your first step toward better health.*

Remember the nursery rhyme, "Sticks and stones may break my bones but words will never hurt me?" Don't kid yourself—words can *kill* you! You will learn about that, not only in this chapter, but throughout the book. And you will learn how to guard yourself against future damage from words, and how to get rid of the repressed emotional dynamite resulting from the word damage of your past.

When you come to the mind-body idea, and really understand its full significance, you will be well on your way to recognizing your psychosomatic health wreckers, and what to do about them.

1

How to recognize the health-wreckers in your life

You must first learn the true meaning of the word *psycho-somatic*. This word has been in our language for over one hundred years; but it is safe to say that very few of us know what it really means. The word was introduced into American medicine by Dr. Flanders Dunbar in 1935, and has been misused and mis-understood ever since, both by physicians and the public. It does not mean only *psychogenic*—"caused by the emotions"; but it includes this meaning in its total significance. Similarly, it does not simply mean *functional*, nor does it just mean *organic*, but it includes both of these meanings as parts of its larger definition. Well, then, what does it *really* mean?

"Psychosomatic disease" properly includes all disease we now call *organic*, and disease we now call *functional*, including the neuroses. This is a tall order, and requires some explanation:

Let us begin by dissecting the word *psychosomatic*. Psycho-somatic is made up of two words, *psyche*, meaning "mind," and *somatic*, referring to the body (soma). It includes both body and mind in one word, one concept. It does not separate the two, and that is the importance of the word. It is impossible to separate the body from the mind.

These are, of course, merely labels, for no such separation exists in nature. Try to imagine a mind walking around without a body—impossible. It is easier to imagine a body walking around without much of a mind, for that would be an imbecile, a low-grade moron, a cretin, a Mongoloid idiot, or a mentally retarded child. But even in such people, there is some degree of mind, and even they suffer both in body and mind, no matter what the disease that afflicts them.

And so we begin to get a glimpse of the true meaning of the word *psychosomatic*. It means "the body-mind unit." It eliminates the artificial separation of body and mind by separate labels, and puts them together in one word as they are together in nature, within ourselves. After all, you can put your finger on your body, but you cannot do the same for your mind. The mind is just a word referring to a particular function of the entire body and, most especially, to the central nervous system. Even there, we are stopped by the labeling confusion.

It is easy enough to say that the function of the kidney is to get rid of the poisons in our blood by passing them along to the outside in the urine. It is likewise easy enough to say that the function of the thyroid gland is the secretion of thyroxine. But do we stop and realize that if the kidneys stop their function, the entire body is poisoned and the mind becomes confused and ceases to think straight? Where, then, is the mind? Is it not as much in the kidney as in the brain? Not really—but it is dependent in part upon proper kidney function. It is closely related to the kidneys.

And if the thyroid gland is removed, or if it stops producing its daily pin-point portion of thyroxine, the mind becomes that of a cretin. Is the mind in the thyroid, then, as well as in the brain? No, but it is certainly dependent upon the proper function of this ductless gland, as it is upon the proper workings of all glands, all organs, all parts of the body. The mind, then, is a function of the entire body. It cannot exist without the body. It is the body. And the body is the mind. These are merely words, artificial separations from the facts of nature, only imperfect ways we use to talk to one another. Unfortunately our language does not always make good sense in this case, and can even destroy us. Certainly, *the abuse of language, and our lack of understanding of language, can cause disease.* And it is only by the correction of this abuse that disease can be brought under control. In part, that is what you will learn in this book. That is what you are learning right now. You are taking the first step, the most important step, when you learn the true meaning of the word *psychosomatic.*

And so, once again, *psychosomatic* refers to the body-mind unit, the inseparable mind-body as it exists in nature, and not as it is found in the dictionary. Begin now to think in terms of your mind-body—the real mind-body (or body-mind, as you wish, since it makes no difference how you arrange the words as long as you really know their true meaning) the total you.

Why we see only in parts

None of us can see *all* there is to see. Even when we look at a painting, for example, we each see it differently. The painter sees the technical factors, the brush strokes, the use of color, the composition, the perspective, the minute factors of the artist's method of handling his medium. The prospective purchaser of a painting sees the picture as an investment, or perhaps as a decoration for his home. The interior decorator sees the possibilities of the painting in a particular room of a particular house, merely as a part of a general color scheme. The museum director may see the painting in its historical context as a possible acquisition for his museum. The dealer in paintings sees the painting in terms of its profit potential, both now and for the future of the artist (and himself as the artist's dealer).

The same is true for everything in our environment. We each see things differently, and we each see only a small part of what there is to be seen. We see in terms of our habits of thinking, our training, our philosophy, our religion, our special capacities for seeing, thinking and feeling; and, most especially, we see things in the way we have been taught to see and think and feel.

A simple example is our response to the American flag. If we are Americans, this can be a stirring sight, stimulating the pulse, perhaps snapping us to attention, sometimes bringing tears to our eyes. The reaction of the Russian to our flag would be quite different. The stimulus is the same, but the behavior, thinking, and feeling of the American and Russian will be different. You have been taught to hate, and you have been taught to love. Once again, we see how we all react differently to the words, symbols, and other aspects of our environment. We not only see things differently, but, individually, we never see all there is to see. We react in a trained, conditioned manner, and we react with our entire bodies, our mind-body unit.

This can be dangerous. It can cause our blood pressure to rise, our pulse to speed up, our arteries to constrict painfully, and many other body changes, some of which may lead to serious disease—the very health wreckers we are talking about. Odd, isn't it, to realize that our training and thinking, our childhood behavior patterns, can cause us to react in self-destructive ways to words, symbols, and everything else! We should learn to understand and control these reactions if we are to safeguard and prolong our lives. We will learn this control as we progress through the simple methods of this book, especially in Chapters 3, 4, and 5.

Functional versus organic problems

What is a functional disease? What is an organic disease? A *functional* disease is said to be one in which the way an organ does its job is impaired, without any structural changes in that organ. I don't believe that it is possible for the function of any part of the body to be disturbed without some organic change, however small. Function depends upon structure (and vice versa), and if the function changes or is impaired, there has been some change in the structure of the diseased tissue. The terms functional and organic are therefore confusing, since *all disease is both functional and organic.* In all probability there is some structural (organ) change, even if only at the basic cellular level beyond the reach of the most carefully designed microscope, at the very outset of every so-called functional disease. All disease, then, is "functional-organic." Here we have the Magic Hyphen, a very important idea in our battle against the harmful effect of the misunderstanding and the misuse of words.

The magic hyphen

When we stop thinking in terms of black or white, either this or that, functional or organic, imaginary or real, psychic or somatic, we will begin thinking in a way that more closely approximates the real world. We now know that there can be no mind without a body, and that there is actually a mind-body unit. You are a mind-body unit, as I am, and as each of us is. Your mind-body unit does everything in a functional-organic way; and when it suffers "disease," the "disease" is psychosomatic.

The magic hyphen puts back together the living facts that our language has artifically separated. The labels that are misapplied to little bits and pieces of our bodies are removed; and a single, hyphenated label is used in their place. The new label more closely represents the truth of oneness of structure and function.

It's all a matter of degree and emphasis

Again I want to caution you about the matter of emphasis, the question of degree. A disease may have a major degree of organic change, or a minor degree. There may be an extensive functional disturbance or a very minor one. There is always both a functional and an organic change, but the degree of each varies from one condition to another, from patient to patient, from time to time, from disease to disease. Just as no two fingerprints are alike, no two patients are alike, and no two diseases are exactly alike.

One of my patients, a very young man of 23, lost his mother from cancer of the bowel. She had a chronic constipation, and finally began to bleed from the rectum. My patient developed chronic constipation, and then rectal bleeding. He made the error of thinking that all constipation and all rectal bleeding represented bowel cancer. His condition was simply bleeding internal hemorrhoids (piles) and improper diet—both easily corrected. But it was not so easy to retrain his thinking, to remove his self-identification with his mother. It was a matter of degree and emphasis, a matter of learning that we are each of us different, and that his constipation and his bleeding were not his mother's constipation and not his mother's bleeding.

The "either-or" error

The magic hyphen helps us get rid of *the either-or error* in our thinking. Nothing is entirely black or entirely white in real life. We must learn to think in terms of shades of gray. Disease is not either functional or organic, psychic or somatic, real or imaginary, but is actually a combination of both, in varying degrees. The mixture may be mostly organic or mostly functional in any organic-functional problem. It may be mostly emotional or mostly somatic, in any psychosomatic condition. It may be mostly real or mostly imaginary in any real-imaginary disturbance. But it is always both, and never either-or.

In the proper use of the word *psychosomatic,* we go a step beyond the hyphen, and eliminate the either-or completely. We must do this in our thinking, in the way we feel and react, as well as on the verbal, written word level. We have been taught to think in black and white, either-or terms, and we must retrain ourselves to think in other terms, ways that more closely approximate the real world in which we live, function, and die. We must do this without delay if we are to function well, live long, and postpone death.

The unity of mind and body

You have now learned the true meaning and origin of the word *psychosomatic.* You have learned the important fact that practically all disease is psychosomatic. This is a valuable revelation, for it puts the control of your problem largely in your own hands. It also puts the responsibility for your future health largely in your own hands.

You now know that your mind and body are a single unit, a mind-body unit. You know that this mind-body unit functions as a single structure. And you know that a change in any part of you may change the function of the entire you. Conversely, a change in the way your body works may change part or all of your body's structure. The way your body is built (structure) and the way it works (function) are simply opposite sides of the same coin. Indeed, they are the same coin.

You can take advantage of this unitary, function-structure idea by learning the simple methods for self-control of your body. You will learn these methods of deep relaxation, guided association, and many others, in later chapters, especially in Chapter 5.

You are now well on your way to recognizing your psychosomatic health-wreckers and soon you will know how to cope with them successfully.

Points to remember:

1. Practically all disease is psychosomatic.
2. All disease is both functional and organic.
3. Use the "Magic Hyphen" to set your thinking straight.
4. Discard the "Either-Or" ways of thinking.
5. Always think in terms of the body-mind unit, and never of just body *or* mind, or body *and* mind.
6. Since your body-mind functions as a unit, control of one automatically gives you control of the other.
7. Words mean different things to each of us.
8. Your body-mind unit reacts to words and symbols largely as you have been taught to react, and the result may be a serious disease.
9. You can retrain your body-mind unit to prevent such disturbances, and to correct those already present.
10. You will soon learn easy methods so that you yourself may control your body-mind structure-function, to help you get rid of your psychosomatic health-wreckers.

Chapter 2

HOW YOUR PERSONALITY
INFLUENCES YOUR HEALTH

If you are to really understand the way psychosomatic problems develop, you will need to understand the normal unfolding of the personality. By now you recognize the fact that many of our adult problems have their origins in our earliest childhood experiences, and some of them can easily be traced back to our infancy. Some of our psychosomatic health-wreckers are not so easily traced back, but did originate in poor feeding habits or poor toilet training. And they must be traced back both on the level of intellectual understanding and on the even more important level of actual reliving of emotionally charged experiences. You will learn how to do just this in Chapters 4 and 5.

We will now trace the development of the common childhood problems, your relationship to your parents and to your earliest environment. Your childhood scars will be uncovered, and you will soon see how the illness of today may be related to the feeding problems, the toilet training, the thumbsucking, the sex development, nightmares and tantrums of your earliest yesterdays.

We will then move on to the personality development of the adolescent years, and you will learn how "adolescent" parents may mark their developing children for life. We will consider the usual personality of an adult, and whether or not anyone is normal. We will consider masochism (self-injury), sadism (injury of

8

others), our changing moral standards, sex practices in the modern society, and many other factors that influence our personality in the formative and the final stages. As we do this, you will see more and more clearly how your developing personality is conditioned, trained, and inadvertently set up for the psychosomatic disorders of childhood and adult life—the very problems from which you now suffer.

Your childhood problems

Psychosomatic disease can begin in infancy. I remember the case of the asthmatic infant who was given up to die at twelve years of age. His asthma had become progressively more severe, increasing from the scattered attacks of infancy to the status asthmaticus of practically continuous wheezing in early adolescence. This child could not complete a single year at school, and spent most of his time in bed fighting for breath.

His mother and father moved from one part of the country to another, following the doctors' advice to seek dry and pollen-free climates, and all to no avail. The condition became progressively worse, and soon the doctors gave up.

When I saw this boy, he was a walking skeleton, and I could understand why he was considered hopeless. Careful laboratory and clinical studies revealed nothing wrong at all. He was normal in all respects, except that he was dying. I told his mother and father that he had only one chance to live. "Your boy," I said, "is allergic to you." This was a difficult thing to tell his parents, for they had given up a great deal by traveling from one part of the country to another in the hope that they might help their son. I advised that he leave them completely, and he was sent to a boardinghouse in Arizona. His parents remained in Tennessee.

The asthma stopped promptly. He breathed easily, with little or no help from medications or physicians, and began to grow and fill out. He grew to over six feet in height, got married, and became a successful lawyer. And now for the final shocker— Arizona is full of pollen, and is probably one of the worst places to go for any respiratory allergy!

This boy was, indeed, allergic to his parents, and it was proven by the recurrence of asthma every time he visited them or when they visited him.

Were you allergic to your parents?

This is obviously an important question. I do not use the term allergic in the usual sense, but rather to indicate a dislike or actual hatred. It is surprising to most of us to learn that we all are ambivalent about our parents, as they are about us. That means that we both love and hate each other. That is normal, so do not be disturbed.

Love and hate, like life and death, are inseparable. We often do not realize this, and unwittingly hurt the ones we love the most. Some parents actually have an unconscious hatred for their children. The overindulgent parent, and the cold parent, without intending to do so, may be harming their youngsters beyond recall.

If we are to really understand the growth of the personality, we must learn something about the relationship of parents and children. This is particularly important if your parents were cold, overindulgent, hostile, sexually frustrated, neurotic, or suffering from continuous anxiety. This just about covers all parents, for stress and its attendant anxiety is a normal part of every adult life—a normal part, therefore, of every child-parent relationship.

The cold parent

When John W. became my patient he was 42 years of age and successful in business. But he was unmarried, unhappy and suffered from chronic constipation and bleeding hemorrhoids. I corrected the hemorrhoids (piles) by injection treatment without surgery. But the constipation proved quite another thing.

The Conflict Check Chart (*see* Chapter 4) revealed the early source of his problem. He had been brought up with every material luxury. Nothing had been denied to him. He was an only child, but there had been a younger sister who died in infancy.

He remembered his parents as they were during his childhood, and they were still alive and "still the same." They were reserved, distant, showed no affection openly, and obviously were afraid to become too attached to a child who might be snatched from them by death at any moment (This was their explanation when I discussed their son's problem with them). But the problem went even deeper, since their own parents had also been cold and aloof, typical pillars of their community who had the time and milk of human kindness for everyone and for every cause except their own children.

Toilet training had been a matter of demanding that the bowel movement be passed on schedule and in the "potty." This training had been entrusted to a nursemaid who thought that the bowel movement was unclean and disgusting. Worse still, she had no children of her own and no love for John.

The result was, that although John carried on the tradition of his family in contributing to charity, he refused to part with his treasured bowel movements. And so, the result was chronic constipation, a psychosomatic health-wrecker that caused bleeding hemorrhoids and great anxiety.

Guided Association Therapy (Chapter 5) and training in relaxation methods, combined with proper diet and other medical measures, corrected the anxiety-related constipation. It also helped to make John a warmer and a better person.

The sexually frustrated parent

We should face the fact that the majority of parents are sexually frustrated. If they were not, the Kinsey report would not show the extensive adultery and promiscuity that it does. When the parents' love life is not adequately satisfied within marriage, their love is transferred to the child. This is obviously not good for the child, and may prevent its normal emotional development and normal personality development.

Mary Ellen was a perfectly beautiful 18-year-old girl, but her father had been her "suitor" since she was a baby. This abnormal attachment resulted from the poor sexual relationship between her father and mother. Her mother had strong religious qualms about sexual intercourse and believed that it was sinful unless intended for "having children." Her husband felt otherwise, and felt the need for sexual contact at frequent intervals. When these were denied to him by his wife, he gave his affection entirely to Mary Ellen, an only child.

Mary Ellen appeared to show a normal interest in boys, but it always stopped short of a kiss, and she had no desire for marriage. "I prefer an older man," she insisted. I was consulted for her severe headaches that followed each date, with nausea and vomiting. Were we dealing with migraine headaches or with an intestinal problem? Neither. We were facing a psychosomatic health-wrecker that originated in the distorted relationship between her parents, the sexual frustration of her father. The whole family needed treatment.

The parent who hates

We have already touched upon this subject when we discussed the child who is allergic to his parents and the converse, the parent who dislikes or actually hates his child. The dislike or hatred may be conscious or unconscious. In most cases the parent is unaware of the feelings or behavior, and the damage is produced in many subtle ways.

Many mothers look upon their daughters as serious rivals for their husbands' affection. A close relationship between father and daughter is a normal development. A jealous or possessive wife may react violently, especially if this is not balanced by a good relationship between a son and his mother. If there is only one child, a daughter who loves her father, the mother may feel that her husband is showing his daughter greater affection and love than he shows to "his own wife."

Mrs. R. L. developed almost the whole gamut of large bowel organ language, and told me, "I can't stomach the way my husband pays attention to *his* daughter." She literally couldn't, and vomited after breakfast each day. This was accompanied by painful gas distention, and "sick headaches."

The great danger in this case was to the emotional development of the child. She became moody, withdrawn, and failed to have regular menstrual periods despite a prefectly normal set of female organs and glands.

The same thing can happen to a boy if his father resents any special attention paid by his wife to their son. But in my experience this is much less frequent.

The overindulgent parent

This is a particularly severe problem in these affluent, permissive days. Many parents who can afford it grant every wish of their children, even their unspoken desires. They overprotect as well as overgratify their children, sheltering them from the jungle reality of life.

These children are not equipped to compete when they are outside the home, even during their school days. Mother or dad may fight their battles with teachers, with other students, and even with their own neighborhood friends. Given no responsibilities, with every whim gratified, and believing that they are to be granted special dispensation throughout life, these children are destined to experience many frustrations and much unhappiness later in life. They are certainly going to develop many psychosomatic problems and neuroses. They may become problem children and find themselves in the children's courts or problem adults in even more serious troubles.

These apparently "model" parents have not learned the importance of training their children to develop a good sense of values, giving only in proportion to the child's efforts to deserve reward, and not lavishly in response to every whim or in the effort to buy the child's affection.

John was a heroin addict, despite the fact of his fine home and good background. He developed this habit during one of the lavish parties his parents provided "at the drop of a hat." At sixteen years of age, this fine boy was well on his way to total self-destruction. He had been provided with every comfort, and nothing had ever been denied to him. His parents told me this to justify their own innocence in this disaster. They were doing a good job of testifying to their guilt.

Less radical personality changes and problems may develop in such children, and when later faced with the frustration and anxiety of real life, the self-destructive tendencies may produce serious psychosomatic health-wreckers.

Your childhood scars

The personality-distorting problems of childhood may originate in such apparently harmless areas as feeding problems, toilet training, thumb sucking, unnecessary guilt about masturbation, nightmares, and tantrums. You have already seen an illustration of the terrible harm that may come from poor toilet training. But there may be much worse consequences than constipation and hemorrhoids. There may be personality changes as serious as becoming a miserly recluse, or lesser degrees of withdrawal and greed. We will discuss each of these childhood scars and see some of the personality changes and health-wreckers that may result.

Toilet training and your future

Our adult attitude toward bowel movements is closely associated with our earliest toilet training. Psychosomatic problems often result from improper early training. There is a great deal of evidence that our attitudes toward our bowels, as they developed in earliest infancy, have an enormous effect on our later adult bowel habits and bowel diseases. But there is also much evidence that the effects go even deeper, damaging and altering the total adult personality.

The child who has a bowel movement at the "right" time and in the "right" place is usually praised and rewarded. If he is rewarded with money, he may later come to think of his bowel movement as valuable—worth money. He ends up both miserly and constipated. He cannot bear to part with either his money or his bowel movement. After all, who can blame the child in an adult body who has been toilet-trained by financial reward when he later refuses to flush money down the drain!

Even when our parents do not connect our bowel movements with a monetary reward, conditioning us to think of them as closely related or of the same value, they make it very obvious that our bowel movement *is* something of value. If it were not so valuable, why all the fuss about the bowel movement at the right time and in the right place?

Think back to your own childhood experiences, or look at the way you handle your own children (the Conflict Check Chart, Chapter 4, will help you do this the easy way). A bowel movement at the wrong time or in the wrong place is punished and scolded. And so, our earliest feelings about our bowel movements become inextricably connected with approval, love, affection, hostility, and something of value.

Our earliest and strongest emotions have to do with food, hunger, and bowel movements—all intestinally based, strong feelings. Is it any wonder that the intestinal tract becomes the sounding board of our emotions? (*See* Chapter 6 for the psychosomatic health-wreckers that result!)

How to avoid toilet training problems

Such problems can be avoided as follows:

1. Do not begin a child's toilet training too early. Fifteen months is the earliest age at which toilet training should start. Some children should not be started until they are even older, and your pediatrician should guide you.

2. Most important, don't get emotional about your child's bowel movements. It is obvious that too much concern over a bowel movement will color your child's thinking about this natural act for all time. This subconscious "thinking" may cause psychosomatic health-wreckers in the intestinal tract (*See* Chapter 6) all through his life. This may already have happened to you, and the simple self-help methods of Chapters 4 and 5 will show you the way out.

Be especially careful if you are a parent who suffers from chronic constipation. You may attach so much importance to your own bowel movements that you become over-anxious about your children's bowel action. You know what happens when you try to force your child to eat. He may resist, refuse food, and use this as a weapon against you. The same thing may occur when he senses the enormous value you place upon his bowel movements.

3. Bowel movement training must always be in a relaxed and friendly atmosphere. There must be no forcing, no strain, no rigid demands, and no emotional reactions other than warmth and friendliness.

Toilet-trained rebellion

The result of poor toilet training may be either rebellion or over-conformity, with many psychosomatic health-wreckers as the final effect. Harry became a rebel, from earliest childhood into adult life. He had been trained to think of his bowel movements as "worth money," since he always got toys or actual cash when he "was a good boy" and "did his duty well." And so, when he went into the business world, he continued to value the wrong things. The Conflict Check Chart and Guided Association (*See* Chapters 4 and 5) showed him that his subconscious mind had been thinking as follows: "If I have been trained to value even bowel movements, certainly everything I do must be of even greater value. I can do no wrong." He became totally ruthless in his private and business life. In adult life he continued to withhold his valuable bowel movements and developed serious constipation, often to the point where the stool had to be removed manually, sometimes with a local anesthetic.

He also withheld his feelings, and never married. He was stingy, gave no quarter in his business dealings, and was thoroughly disliked by everyone.

Personality changes can obviously run very deep when early childhood toilet training is badly managed.

The toilet-trained conformist

We do not know why some children react by submission and complete conformity, while others become rebels. The same opposite poles of reaction are seen in the feeding problems. When one child rebels and refuses to eat, another child may become a docile or even a compulsive eater.

Mary became a perfectionist and a complete conformist. She had been so rigorously toilet trained, that she carried over this training into all phases of life. She was punctual, tried for constant perfection, demanded perfection of others, and could not stand the slightest deviation from "the best" in others. She was an anxious, unhappy person since she could not find a man who lived up to her difficult, toilet-trained standards. She never married and lived a life of total frustration with many psychosomatic problems related to her intestinal tract.

The simple, self-help methods of Chapters 4 and 5 uncovered the roots of her psychosomatic symptoms, and helped her get rid of them. You will soon learn these self-help methods yourself.

Did you masturbate?

If you did not, you were certainly not average, and perhaps you were not normal in the sense of the statistical norm. Practically everyone has masturbated, and some men continue to masturbate even after they are happily married. This can be normal. It is normal for both men and women to masturbate from childhood on.

Those of us who were taught that masturbation would make us ill or feeble-minded, may have been left with serious emotional personality problems. The famed psychiatrist Karl Menninger tells us that ". . . the boy who refrains from masturbation out of fear and guilt is more unstable, more subject to physical and nervous breakdown, and more likely to develop character disturbances than is the boy who is able to masturbate without feelings of guilt or to control such guilt feelings as masturbation arouses in him."

The important fact for the child and his parents to realize is that masturbation is normal. After all, handling the sex organs gives pleasurable sensations, and it is natural to do whatever gives us pleasure. The child must never be told that there is harm in this behavior. If he has heard that masturbation is harmful, he must be set straight in his thinking.

Serious personality problems may result if these misconceptions are not corrected. There may be a morbid fixation on sex, and perversions, frigidity, or impotence may result.

Howard became quite impotent and required careful reassurance after his problem was uncovered by the Conflict Check Chart (Chapter 4) and treated by Guided Association therapy (Chapter 5). He had been told repeatedly, by his father, that "boys who play with themselves shrink down there until it almost disappears." He accepted these words quite literally and expected his genitals to shrink.

Mary enjoyed masturbation, having learned about the clitoris from a nursemaid. Her mother discovered the relationship with the nursemaid and literally threw the nurse out of their home, shrieking, "you have ruined my daughter. Now she can never be a normal wife." Mary was seven years old, and the words seared themselves into her mind. She married, but she did not expect to become a normal wife. She was frigid and finally told her husband that she could not bear to be touched by him. Her habits soon changed in the direction of homosexuality, although she now had a fine little son. This was a very serious problem for both husband and wife, and the psychosomatic difficulties that arose in both of them brought them to my attention.

Feeding problems

The reactions to forced feeding of the infant or older child may be generally in the direction of rebellion or overconformity, exactly as described for the toilet training problems. For the infant, one of the earliest, and perhaps the most important, evidences of love, security, and warmth of emotion is in the feeding process. The breast-nipple is the symbol and the fact of such love, security, and warmth.

At a later age (or right from the beginning in most cases), the bottle substitutes for the breast. This is not a good substitute, either for the body or for the emotions, since the baby will be healthier both in personality and body if breast-fed.

Good food, regularly provided in an atmosphere of love, is important to the development of a feeling of affection, warmth, and security. Hostility, impatience, or neglect at feeding time may produce anxiety and a deep and abiding feeling of insecurity and uncertainty. The child must be made to feel wanted, loved, sheltered, but must be neither weaned forcibly nor fed forcibly.

Mary was my patient at 35 years of age, and she had been married for 12 years. There were no children. Her husband had been well-to-do when they married, but later lost his business. The reduced income called for "belt-tightening," and she felt deprived in every way. This feeling of lack and lessening affection brought back to her mind some of her early childhood experiences. She felt the same sense of neglect that she had experienced "from infancy on" when her mother "had more important things to do than worry about my food." She had been bottle-fed, and her mother's many social activities left her more or less to her own devices at feeding time practically throughout her entire childhood and into adolescence. A succession of maids, none of whom gave her affection or "any special care," completed the picture.

Her remembered sense of neglect, hostility, and indifference combined with the present need for "belt-tightening," resulted in very expressive *organ language* of the stomach. She gradually developed a peptic ulcer.

Some of us later seek the security that had been denied us during our earliest feeding experiences by overeating to the point of gross obesity. Others rebel against the way our mothers force us to eat during childhood by eating very little and badly when we "grow up."

Prevention is the best medicine, and this is easily provided by an atmosphere of warmth, gentleness, love, and care at feeding time. The problem is with the mother, and not with the child. Her attitude must be that of TLC—Tender Loving Care, if her child's personality is not to be warped. Breast feeding of the infant is best, wherever possible. Try to be happy and hide your daily cares when mealtimes come. Do not discuss the anxieties and problems of life during these times. There should be obvious warmth and love between the parents as much as possible, and especially at mealtimes. Do not force-feed your children and do not neglect their needs. Sometimes this calls for walking a difficult, thin line between love and neglect, but it must be done.

Feeding problems obviously are important determinants of personality development. Love, life, death—all enter through the mouth.

Thumb-sucking and your personality

Thumb-sucking is normal. As you have seen, the mouth is our first source of sensual pleasure, especially for the breast-fed infant. As the infant grows, there will be times when he explores his world and himself, and one of these times is when he puts his thumb in his mouth and sucks contentedly. He is imitating the very pleasurable nipple-sucking. When he "grows up," he will continue this sensual pleasure by substituting pipes, cigars, cigarettes, or even food in general, for the breast and nipple. And the adult male, during sexual intercourse, returns contentedly to the breast of his beloved—returns to his infancy and his first source of sensual pleasure. This is normal, just as normal as thumb-sucking.

So, do not scold. Do not pull your child's thumb out of his mouth, and do not warn him that his teeth will grow crooked. Let a dentist correct this problem if it develops. In most cases, if you avoid excessive attention to thumb-sucking and do not criticize or scold, it will gradually give way before your substitute of warmth, love, and affection.

If you have become a problem smoker of cigarettes and are correctly worried about the possibility of lung cancer, it may help you to realize that smoking is an infantile reaction to life's anxieties. You can do better than react at the infantile level. After all, you are an adult and should learn to face and control your problems rather than retreating to your mother's breast in the cigarette-nipple substitute. It's okay to be a thumb-sucker, but it is not okay to be a dying cigarette-sucker. After all, what is a "sucker?"

You and your childhood nightmares

The adult personality is determined by many factors, but most especially by everything that happens from infancy on. This includes the dreams and the nightmares of our childhood. The anxiety and fear of the child is very real, and often is expressed in terrifying nightmares. When I remember the cruelty of childhood fairy tales, and couple this with the sadism and violence of television and the motion pictures, I find it remarkable that most children do not have even worse nightmares.

Punishment or threat of punishment may leave deep levels of anxiety and may even produce fear of our parents. These may be expressed during sleep and, in later life, in terms of hostility and repressed anxiety. The ultimate effect may well be a psychosomatic illness.

Harold had frequent nightmares. This sensitive ten-year-old youngster actually realized that the "horrible monster" of his dreams resembled his father. Curiously enough, it was not that his father had punished him excessively or even physically. The fact was that his father was aloof from his children, lived entirely for his profession, and never struck them in anger or otherwise. The problem was with the mother. She constantly threatened Harold that his father would "take a strap" to him if he didn't behave. In his recurring nightmares Harold was suspended by a strap that cut into his "middle," while the monster simply made horrible faces at him.

Serious personality disturbances may result if such dreams are not halted, explained, and the anxiety dispelled by an explanation of the reality. If not checked, these anxiety-laden personality changes may cause even more serious disease in later life.

Stress in adolescence

Adolescence is a difficult time. It is particularly trying when the adolescent child is guided by equally adolescent parents. We should face the fact that most adults are merely children in adult bodies. This is the fact even when these adolescent adults become parents. And so we are faced with the cruel reality of adolescent children versus adolescent parents.

None of us is mature at all levels of our development or behavior. Our patterns of behavior are imitated by our children, leaving them with ultimate levels of immaturity very much like our own. The cure for our children therefore must begin with us. As we locate and change our own immature response patterns, we will be better equipped to guide and correct the personality and behavior patterns of our youngsters. This chapter helps you understand and get rid of your own psychosomatic health-wreckers while preventing them in your children.

Adolescence is the time when our sex glands begin to function more actively. It is the time when sexual fantasies and masturbation become more frequent. It is often a time of timidity, shame, anxiety, and inferiority feelings. It is a time when conflicting codes of behavior must be resolved by the youngster. This is particularly distressing in the management of sexual feelings, conflicts between school and parental codes of behavior, religious conflicts, personal ethics set against standards of group acceptance and general conflicts with the parents themselves. It is a time when the seeds of serious psychosomatic disease are often planted.

Resentment of parental authority

Adolescents usually resent their parents. Often they consider them "square," stupid, and poorly informed. They cannot accept their parents' moral, religious, or ethical standards. It is best to counter this tendency as early as possible by advising our children that we are as anxious as they are to "cut the umbilical cord." We must make them feel that we only wish to give them the benefit of our experience and, most especially, our mistakes. We must not pretend to be God. We must not pretend to know all the answers and must be willing to learn from our children. At the same time, we also must provide standards of behavior, making it clear that we are doing this only so that they may learn to live for themselves when the time comes.

Many parents find it difficult to let go of their children, and this can be a serious source of trouble for both parent and child. Mrs. R. L. illustrates this. She leaned upon her son and daughter even more than they leaned upon her. Both children were very bright and recognized "Mother's need for a crutch." Father had died when the children were eight and twelve, the son being the older. It was then that Mother began to develop many psychosomatic problems. The children helped a great deal by their insight and their willingness to cooperate with Mother while maintaining their own direction of personality development.

But often the children are pulled deeper and deeper into their parents' problems, their parents' needs for emotional dependency. When this occurs, the children may suffer more than the parents. They deserve better.

Do not expect too much at any age

We are apt to treat our children as adults before they are ready for it. Often there is a wide range of dependency and insecurity one day, and a demand for independence the next; this is quite typical of the adolescent. We must understand and go along with these evidences of anxiety. Do not overrate or underrate your children, and do not expect too much from them. Do not demand love. Do not demand the highest possible school grades. Do not demand perfect social and ethical behavior. After all, although you want them to be better than yourself, how perfect are you?

Conformity versus nonconformity

The adolescent, just as every other age level, tries to conform to the customs and manners of his own age group. These forms of behavior and dress may seem strange to us who are older and are often quite different from our own ideas of good form but they are very important to the youngsters. We should not object if our child wants to be like other children in his clothing, speech, and social behavior, unless these are destructive habits. Naturally, we do not wish them to become narcotic addicts, or even to smoke cigarettes—both are deadly. Nor do we wish them to be sexually promiscuous. But whether we wish it or not, they will follow the leader, dress in the "uniform" of their group, speak the "hip" language, read the "hip" books, dance the "hip" dances.

Conformity to nonconformity

To a large degree, we see strange behavior in so many youngsters in a group that the final effect is conformity to nonconformity. The bearded Zen pretender, the sneakers and half-length, torn-margin blue jeans, the Beatle haircut, have all become so common that they are more usual than unusual. This is conformity to nonconformity.

And so we have the curious phenomenon of the conforming rebels. These tendencies should not be curbed. Individuality is most important for good character and personality development, even if the individuality is patterned in a trend of conforming to nonconformity.

Sex codes

We have already illustrated how our earliest feeding and bowel training patterns influenced our later sex development. The adolescent may already be confused and anxious about the sex act, perhaps as a result of little or no information during his earlier development. Parents often shy away from answering their children's questions about sex. This is a mistake. Such questions should be answered honestly and just as fully as the child's mind can absorb. The time to provide sex information is when the child asks for it, regardless of his age.

And then there are the problems that arise when a large family occupies small quarters with no privacy for the parents' bedroom. This is an unfortunate situation, and it often leads to the comparing of notes with other youngsters and the early implantation of misinformation. Children should be educated in the basic biology of sex in their early school years as part of a sex-hygiene program. This program should continue throughout their school training into high school and college. It should be considered a normal part of every child's training both at school and at home. Once it is seen for what it is, a normal part of life, it will be shorn of its mysticism, its concealment, its eroticism, and its "forbidden fruit" character. This is the best possible basis for normal personality development.

It is impossible to pass a valid moral judgment on adolescent sex play. But it is certainly true that the potential dangers to the personality resulting from promiscuity are far greater than those following sex patterns that stop short of actual intercourse. This is most true of the high school age group and is generally valid for the college group as well. No general rules for "normal" sex patterns can be provided.

Naturally, it is best to understand our sex urges and recognize the fact that this drive is an underlying force in all our activities. Repression or distortion of this drive may later cause serious, psychosomatic health-wreckers. That is why marriage and a normal sex outlet should be made available to everyone as early as possible. But marriage is not for children and adolescents. A too-early marriage will cause more psychosomatic problems than it will solve. The sex problem is not easily solved, and certainly not by generalizations. Each youngster must be advised by loving and understanding parents as the questions arise. If there is enough real affection and genuine information at home, there is apt to be less disturbed sex action away from the home.

Adolescents and their parents

The relationship between the adolescent and his parents is often strained. Most adults find it difficult to alter their own patterns of thinking to accept the strange behavior of their children. Flexibility, understanding and love, and especially, forgiveness are all essential. Always remember that your own behavior seemed strange to your parents. And if you were a paragon of virtue (or have conveniently forgotten your own behavior), don't expect your children to be exactly as good as you were. The probability is that you were not altogether perfect. Do not expect any better from your own children. The demand for perfection will only lead to over-conformity and rigidity of thinking and behavior, or rebellion and all its attendant problems.

Joan rebelled against strict parental discipline. Her parents did not think that a high school girl should be allowed to date more than once a week, and they insisted that she be home no later than midnight. They forgot that every automobile is a potential love-nest on wheels and that motels and hotels are freely available at all hours. Joan was soon pregnant, and an abortion was performed in another State. She was a sexual cripple when I saw her, frigid in her marriage, unhappy and full of anxiety, her menstrual periods occurring at very frequent intervals, and always associated with "sick headaches." She was then 31, and this was her second marriage. Prolonged treatment was required (as described in Chapters 4 and 5), and her second marriage was saved by an understanding, forgiving and very intelligent husband who was patient and considerate throughout the treatment.

The moral of our story is that: 1. Parents must provide love and understanding at all ages. 2. They must provide friendship. 3. They must provide intelligent information on sex at all ages, either directly or through books. 4. They must be neither over-indulgent nor overly strict. It is a difficult, tight, and high wire to walk, but it must be walked by all parents who want their children to develop with a relatively healthy personality, and without becoming prone to psychosomatic health wreckers.

What is a mature adult?

This is a king-size question, and there is no easy answer. The average adult is a grown-up child, often halted at the maturity level of the adolescent. The same arguments of permissive- versus authority-directed levels of behavior that range at all other stages of our development may be considered at the adult level. Should the adolescent be allowed to drink alcohol, to smoke, to have sexual intercourse, even under controlled conditions? Should the adult drink, smoke, or even have sexual intercourse outside of the marriage bed? It is important to answer these questions—important to each of us—since worry and guilt about our own behavior is a basic cause of the psychosomatic health-wreckers.

But there are no standards of "normality," either for personality or behavior. There are laws, which are often broken in private; and no one is considered to have committed a crime until he has been caught, convicted, and sentenced. Even then, the guilt is usually placed on the doorstep of society rather than the individual.

Are we all masochistic? Are we all sadistic? The answer is "yes." It is only a matter of degree. When we make love, we pinch, bite, and some of us find pleasure in other ways of hurting the one we love. This is sadism. And we often enjoy being hurt, or even imposing suffering on ourselves. This is masochism.

So far, then, the average person is basically a criminal, is sadistic and masochistic. Is the mature person religious? Most of us, and especially our politicians, give lip service to religion, but there it ends. There are few practicing Christians, if we consider the teachings of Christ as Christianity. How many of us would give up our wordly goods and follow Him? And in terms of the teachings of Moses, how many of us have not broken one or more of the Ten Commandments? If the Kinsey report is to be believed, we are all of us guilty.

How many of us are motivated by prestige and power drives? All of us. Since these drives can be satisfied only by lying, cheating, taking every advantage of our competitors to the point of driving them out of business (standard operating business "ethics"), and sometimes only by stealing, we are all of us guilty of the gradual daily "murder" of our fellow-man. We are irreligious, destructive, without compassion.

The tyranny of sex drives the average man and woman into adultery. This is a statistical fact, and makes each of us a criminal according to the law, and guilty of a crime against God according to our religion.

Since laws are designed to protect property first and human values only as an after-thought, it would seem that man considers material possessions as more important than his body and his mind. The man who steals a loaf of bread usually goes to jail. The man who "steals" millions within the framework of high level politics or stock market machinations usually goes free. Read the daily newspaper! If he gives some of it to charity, he is a respected member of his community. He may even be elected to high office. Did you ever file an income tax return? If you did, you probably made deductions that were not justified by the facts. We all do. By law, therefore, you are a criminal.

The average adult is a criminal

And so we come to the obvious conclusion that—in terms of the demands of our society and our religion—the average adult is a criminal. I am speaking of the average, mature adult. I am speaking of the respected and honored members of our community and our world.

We can come to only one conclusion. We must either change

ourselves or our society. We must change ourselves or our religion. We must change ourselves or our laws. I would suggest that we must change all of these, but most especially ourselves, if we are to be reasonably healthy. If we do not, we will suffer from guilt, the inescapable realization that we are hurting ourselves and others every day of our lives, and that we often most especially hurt those we should love the most. Psychosomatic disease will result in every case!

What is the solution?

A mature compromise between our basic animal nature and our brain's special capacity to make us better than we are is our goal in our search for maturity. We should be freed from our guilt. We will then be well on our way to release from our psychosomatic symptoms. (Chapters 4 and 5 will show you how to accomplish this!) We should be able to give and receive love. We should be able to work productively in our society and get some satisfaction from our work. We should stop punishing ourselves for the poor training of our childhood and its resulting guilt and hypocrisy in later life. It is this self-punishment—unrecognized at the subconscious level—that later causes the symptoms of our psychosomatic health-wreckers. This book provides a health-directed solution to this problem—simple, do-it-yourself methods to locate these sore spots of your childhood training and immaturity. It provides a program you can follow to get results in ridding yourself of your psychosomatic health-wreckers.

We can change our own body-mind reactions within our short lifetime by using the methods of this book, but we must expect that society will take many generations to catch up with the most enlightened individuals.

What will your characteristics be in the next stage of maturity?

(a) You will be released from your childhood patterns of training and behavior.

(b) You will understand and accept your basic animal nature. You will learn to live with it while gradually changing your behavior patterns to approximate those of your human potential.

(c) You will escape your ego, your basic and well-trained

selfishness, to some degree. You will then feel compassion for others and will be capable of giving of yourself and of your possessions to help those who are less fortunate.

(d) You will not wish to hurt others.

Points to remember:

1. Childhood behavior patterns, experiences, and training all determine later organ language and the nature of your psychosomatic problems.
2. Your childhood scars, resulting from feeding problems, toilet-training, thumb-sucking, sex development, nightmares, tantrums, etc., are all important in your present psychosomatic health problems.
3. Your personality development patterns of adolescence are also factors in your present problems.
4. Sex standards (or lack of standards), religious and ethical training (if any), and the customs of your own social group influence your developing personality and its effect on your body-mind health.
5. You have learned to recognize maturity and immaturity, and the effects of immaturity on your health.
6. You have also learned the true pattern of maturity, as distinguished from the imitation maturity of our society.
7. You have learned the characteristics of the truly superior man and the goal for your future personality development.
8. And now you know what you must do to achieve that goal, and that you will eliminate your psychosomatic health-wreckers in the process.

Chapter 3

LEARNING TO KNOW
WHAT YOUR BODY IS TELLING YOU

Organ language

You are now familiar with the term *organ language*. You know that your body speaks without words, and tells you what is wrong in its own way. It speaks with symptoms such as pain, itching, diarrhea or constipation, headache, difficulty in swallowing or breathing, and in many other ways.

This is the way your body expresses feelings or thoughts that cannot be brought to your attention in any other way. It is a kind of code. We must learn this code if we are to recognize the underlying, emotional push buttons of the past. We must learn this code if we are to understand and correct the complaint of the "talking" organ.

Which organ speaks?

Why does one part of the body speak and not another? This is an interesting question, and you will begin to really understand the answer when you come to the chapters on Guided Association (5) and on the Conflict Check Chart (4). You will learn still more about organ language with each succeeding section, especially when you read about stomach and intestinal problems and about heart anxiety and its symptoms. For the time being, you need to know that as we go through life we record everything that happens to us. We record these events in full color with all sounds, odors, feelings, and every other sensation that we experienced at the time they happened. If we felt pain, that pain sensation is recorded as faithfully as if it had been grooved on a

record. And all these sensations and feelings of our past are
waiting to be replayed, consciously or unconsciously.

Sometimes we do not want to relive distressing episodes of
our past. No matter; if we encounter something resembling one of
the striking factors of the disturbing past situation, our mind
begins to replay the whole scene. It is just as if the needle had
been dropped into the groove, guided there by the duplicating
sight, sound, or emotion of the present. For example, let us suppose that a car ran over your beloved dog when you were six.
You saw the accident, and you rushed over to your dying pet,
and picked him up in your arms. You cried as if your little heart
would break. The driver had stopped, and he tried to console you.

"He ran in front of me, and I couldn't help it." These words,
and every sight, sound, touch, odor, all sensations and feelings of
that painful moment engrave themselves on your brain forever.

And now let us suppose that you are 37 years old, or 47, or
60 (remember—it's recorded *forever*), and you hear the words,
"*I couldn't help it.*" Your unconscious mind brings back the emotions connected with the incident of the six-year-old child you
once were. This does not necessarily mean that you will instantly
recall all the sensations and feelings of that time, but it does mean
that you will feel the pain and anxiety and tears of that event.
You may not know why. You probably will not know why. But
the words, "I couldn't help it," will be emotionally disturbing to
you, even if they were spoken when someone merely stepped
on your toe in a crowded street. Your reaction may therefore be
all out of proportion to the present situation. You want to
know why, and you will think, "Ye gods, but my nerves are on
edge today."

If this is restimulated by your husband when he spills the
coffee on the dining room tablecloth and says "I couldn't help
it,"—your violent reaction may lead to an equally violent argument, and perhaps worse.

This is body language. It is often "spoken" when your
personality and reaction patterns are not sufficiently developed to
allow you to handle emotionally charged problems in any other
way. The organ "speaking" is the one that was involved in the
original emotionally charged situation. It may be your tear
glands, and you will cry, as in the previous example. If you had a
violent headache after your little dog was killed, your brain may

"speak" now through the organ language of headache or a disabling migraine.

This may occur every time you encounter any of the key sensations, words, or feelings of the original episode. An automobile accident, actually seen or reported on television, radio, or in the newspapers—the words, "I couldn't help it," the sight of a dead animal in the road—any one of these may reactivate the emotions of the six-year-old child you once were; and the organ language of the past speaks again.

On the other hand, it may be that your mother always reacted to emotionally disturbing situations by vomiting, diarrhea, or, possibly, painful mentrual periods. If you identify yourself strongly with your mother, your organ language may be similar to hers.

If you have a weak, poorly functioning or otherwise diseased organ, your emotional distress may "speak" through that organ. You may have been born with a poorly functioning organ or body system, such as the child who is "allergic" and wheezes every time his allergy is activated. This "allergy" may be activated by his emotions as easily as by pollen, house dust, or ragweed. He will then wheeze and have difficulty breathing, as his bronchial tubes go into spasm, speaking their organ language. If the physician does not understand the language, the patient will be treated for his symptoms rather than for the underlying emotional problem. That is why it is so important for you to understand your own organ language; know when your body is speaking to you, what it is trying to say, and how to answer. This book teaches you how to answer.

The sounding board of the emotions

The intestinal tract is known to all physicians as the *sounding board of the emotions*. It is the system that responds most frequently and most violently when we are disturbed. It is the system that speaks to us when we have difficulty in swallowing. It is saying, and we may actually put it into words, "I can't swallow that." Or we may simply feel a "ball" in the throat, and we know that we really "can't swallow that." This sensation of a ball is due to spasm of the esophagus, the tube that carries food from the mouth to the stomach.

Or our stomach may say, "I can't stomach that," and vomits.

Again, we may speak the actual words, or we may merely vomit, trying to throw off the emotionally distressing problem in that way. This is part of the organ language of the stomach. The stomach has more to say in some cases and may be so "vocal" as to speak with pain, cramps, vomiting, indigestion, heartburn, nausea, or other evidences to the effect that it "can't stomach that."

Our stomach may be so distressed that it speaks the ultimate words, "I wish I were dead." And then we may hemorrhage or perforate an ulcer.

Our large bowel speaks its own language and speaks often. Poor toilet training may have left you with the idea that your stool has great value (*See* Chapter 2), and you now refuse to part with it—constipation is the result. Or—in rebellion against your mother's rigid toilet training—the adult "you" may go to the other extreme, your bowel now protesting by overactivity of stool, mucus, and perhaps even bleeding.

Your large bowel may speak with violent cramps. Your small bowel may do the same. Any part of your intestinal tract may respond with its own symptom language when disturbed by an anxiety problem of past or present.

From the heart

Our heart is often represented in the lexicon of organ language. The heart speaks primarily in terms of pain. You may have a heartache, and you will say so. Or your heart may say it for you in no uncertain terms. Mothers may say that their children are a "heartache." I remember a mother who used this term often when speaking of her two "little girls." They were 24 and 25, and far from little in any sense. They had left home in their teens in rebellion against an overly strict, puritanical environment without love from their parents, who lived in an atmosphere of mutual silent reproach. The girls' search for love led them to promiscuity, bordering on prostitution. This mother's emotional "heartache" was genuine, based on constant anxiety and guilt over her daughters, actual hatred for her husband, and an unspoken desire to atone by death.

Her heart spoke with coronary spasm, *angina pectoris*, and she both feared and wished for a fatal "heart attack."

The voice of the lungs

Our lungs may speak to us by cough, pain in the chest, or spasm of the tubes that carry the air to all parts of our lungs—the bronchial tubes. There may be other forms of lung language, but these are the most common.

Asthma is the most frequent diagnosis when the lungs speak. The wheeze may be mild, or so severe that death is threatened or occurs. When the bronchial tubes go into spasm and the mucus accumulates in these tubes, the struggle for breath is horrible to behold.

Harold was such a patient, and his lungs spoke violently and often. Finally his condition got so bad that it was practically continual (*status asthmaticus*). Harold was 24 when I saw him. He could not stand his wife, and this was his way of protesting his unhappiness. He soon lost his job, and his wife had to go to work. Fortunately there were no children, and I recommended a trial separation. This was so successful that both Harold and his wife agreed to a divorce as the best solution. They both subsequently remarried. Sad to say, Harold could not stand his second wife any better than his first, and the asthma spoke again and again and resulted in a second divorce. The answer lay in adequate psychotherapy, and Harold finally agreed.

The nervous system speaks

Headache is a major voice in brain organ language. "You are a headache to me," is a common phrase. The brain says the same, and the headache may be very severe, a true migraine. Spasm of the blood vessels of the brain may be the result of stress, anxiety, past or present emotionally charged problems. The reduced blood flow results in headache.

Some headache "voices" are so loud and insistent that they are "overheard" by the sensitive intestinal tract, causing nausea and vomiting. This combination of organ language can be very disabling.

Our entire central nervous system may speak, saying, "I can't take any more." Then we are faced with the organ language of depression, withdrawal, self-induced failure, submission, morbid consideration of suicide, and, perhaps, actual suicide—the ultimate in body language. In some cases there may be self-induced paralysis or weakness of a limb or of the entire body, making work impossible. This is the way the body speaks through the nerves and muscles, to say, "I can't take any more."

The voice from the fortress of fat

If you have become overweight in rebellion against the world, against your parents, against your husband, the voice in your fatty fortress is saying, "You don't love me." Obesity is often evidence of an emotional protest. It is the organ language of the body metabolism, the mouth crying out for a kiss, a caress, the mother's nipple—in a word, for love. This is the most common expression of organ language known to medicine. Unfortunately, however, it is rarely recognized to be organ language, and the voice is not heard.

Treatment with fad diets, multicolored pills, and the like can be only temporarily successful, if at all. The patient may lose weight for a short time, and then will return to the usual diet and emotional patterns. She returns to her fortress of fat, and the voice from within moans desperately and unheard, crying for love. These lost souls will be helped only when we listen and respond. Chapter 8 tells you how to listen, what your body is trying to say, and how to respond.

The language of arthritis

Bone and joint problems may be a protest against the stress of life. No one can expect the arthritic cripple to work. And so the body once again says, "You can have it. I can't take it any more." Arthritis is not well understood, but we know that there is often a close relationship between cortisone and arthritis. And we do know that our special glandular (adrenocortical) system of hormone regulation is closely related to stress and fear. We also know that the patient who receives such cortisone hormones may undergo dramatic changes in personality and outlook at the same time that the arthritis responds. There may even be excessive and unnatural happiness, or a swing to a deep depression, or a mental breakdown. This is an excellent example of the body-mind reacting as a unit. It is organ language of the total body-mind. For that matter, all organ language is more correctly described as a body language, or body-mind language. And so, once again and always, the voice of the body-mind is heard throughout the land.

Colloquial language and organ language

Examples of how the counterparts of our organ language are expressed at the verbal level of our daily speech habits are the following:

Heartache	I'd rather let go
You are a heartache	You give me a pain
My job is a heartache	You gripe me
Chicken-hearted	I could vomit
Light-hearted	I can't swallow that
Lion-hearted	I can't stomach that
Soft-hearted	That gets a load off my chest
You are a headache	It makes my flesh creep
My job is a headache	I could cry
I feel shaky	My nerves are on edge
I feel all-gone	I can't take any more
(I have an all-gone feeling)	You don't love me (a cry of total body despair)
He is spineless	
He has guts	
I can't handle that	I wish I were dead!

You will find many more examples as you go through this book, and will hear them each day if you listen closely to those about you. Such expressions are closely paralleled in other languages, especially German and French. The fact that they are colloquial, generally accepted terms in daily universal use, shows their close kinship with body function.

Organ language and the silent level

The "Silent Level" is the level of the emotions. The level of the emotions is the thalamus and the hypothalamus, the most ancient, animal levels of our brain. The newer level of the brain, the most recently developed, is the cortex, and of all animals, man has the best developed cortex. This is the thinking level, the word level, the level of ideas, abstractions, theories. This is the level of verbal language, while the older part of the brain, the thalamus and the hypothalamus, is the level of organ language. Organ language is non-verbal, although you have seen that there are verbal counterparts in our daily, colloquial language. Organ language is the language of the emotions. Organ language is the language of feelings at the Silent Level. I call it the Silent Level because there are primarily feelings rather than words at this level.

But when organ language is expressed, it is far from silent. The disturbed feelings, the charged emotions, the exploded dynamite of the Silent Level, send out their shock waves throughout the body to explode as tears, cries of despair or rage, violence, disturbed intestinal, heart, or brain function, disturbances in any and all organs and tissues of our bodies. It is then that we see organ language in action. It is then that we see the psychosomatic health-wreckers at work.

To become well, we must probe this Silent Level and release the repressed, walled-in pus of past emotional infections. We must let off steam. We must explode the emotional dynamite of our earliest unhappiness, our earliest pain and stress. We do this with the aid of the Conflict Check Chart (which leads us to the problem times of our past) and the Guided Association sessions, which enable us to relive these times and release the repressed Silent Level emotions. The time has come now to learn more about these methods, so that you may begin to rid yourself of your psychosomatic health wreckers. In the very next chapter I will start you on the road to recovery by showing you how to come to grips with and defeat your health-wreckers.

Points to remember:

1. Your body speaks without words, telling you what is wrong.
2. If you know how to listen, you will hear this organ language, and know how to respond.
3. You cannot rid yourself of your psychosomatic health-wreckers unless you learn to hear and understand organ language.

4. The Silent Level is the level of the emotions. When the Silent Level speaks, it speaks explosively through organ language.
5. You experience *controlled,* Silent Level explosions by means of Guided Association therapy to rid yourself of the repressed, emotional dynamite.

Chapter 4

HOW TO COME TO GRIPS WITH AND BRING YOUR HEALTH-WRECKERS UNDER CONTROL

You are now prepared to tackle your psychosomatic health-wreckers. Let's see what we have accomplished to this point:

1. You have learned how to recognize these changes in your body-mind, and you have grasped the significance of thinking in terms of a body-mind unit. Never again will you be troubled by the "either-or" error. You have mastered the Magic Hyphen, and leaped across the functional versus organic chasm. This understanding of the body-mind unity is the basic first step toward mastering your psychosomatic health wrecker-problems.

2. You are now well versed in the ways your personality developed from infancy to the present moment. You have faced and understood the origins of your childhood problems and have looked squarely upon your repressed childhood scars.

3. You are now well qualified to understand your basic sex development.

4. You have learned the criteria for maturity and have a definite goal to shoot for in your future development. Significantly, you have learned that no one is fully mature in all areas. You will now neither overrate nor underrate yourself, and this will help you get rid of unwarranted inferiority complexes. This feeling of inferiority is a source of worry that may cause many psychosomatic symptoms, especially headaches.

You have learned that we are all basically animals and will accept that part of you that thinks and behaves like an animal.

But you also know that you can be better than you are, and that man has a greater potential for mature behaviour than any other animal. Using the methods of this book, and especially those of this Chapter and the next, you may even become so superior in your personality and behaviour, so superior in your sense of values, that you may become almost God-like. This change will gradually develop as you practice your Guided Association each day together with the other treatment methods you will soon learn.

5. Having now realized that you are now neither better nor worse than the average person, you may move forward to the "better" zone without the guilt burden of unhappy past behaviour patterns.

6. You have also learned Organ Language. You know that your body is speaking to you whenever it is disturbed. And you know that the disturbance may have originated in your infancy, your childhood, or adolescence. It may have been reactivated by some present incident connected by your never-forgetting Silent Level to the original emotion-laden past experience. This is the way many psychosomatic symptoms develop, and you will soon learn how to trace them down and get rid of them.

7. You know now that your brain's Silent Level has recorded all your past experiences, especially those that were painful or unpleasant, sad or tragic; and that those records must be replayed at a conscious level to get rid of their repressed dynamite. You will learn more about how to do this when you read the simple methods of Guided Association therapy in the very next chapter. But first you must learn about the remarkable Conflict Check Chart and what it can do for you.

The conflict check chart and how it works for you

Before you use this chart, you should see your family doctor to rule out or bring under control those organic elements of your psychosomatic problem that require his attention. Surgical correction must be used where required. Medicines may be needed to keep things in check until you have learned how to do without them. Or you may have conditions like diabetes, thyroid overactivity or underactivity, or some other disease that requires very special medicines. Don't try to make your own diagnosis. Don't try to treat yourself or even to use these methods of psychosomatic therapy until you have consulted your physician.

The Conflict Check Chart helps you to locate the emotionally disturbing patterns of your entire lifetime. Look it over carefully before trying to answer the simple questions. A "Yes" or "No" will suffice. But even a Yes or No takes thought, and you must not enter anything until you have resolved to be entirely truthful with yourself. If you are not truthful, you are only cheating yourself.

You already know the purpose of the Check Chart. It is a simple device to review your life from infancy to the present. It is a simple method to locate the emotional disturbances of your past. Until you do locate the times when you were sad, distressed, hurt, violent or violently treated, in pain, sick, suffered loss—in short, *all times of emotional distress*—you cannot proceed with the release of such repressed pain or grief. The Conflict Check Chart points out where the probes must go to release the pus of your past. When these old emotional abscesses are drained, you will be a healthier person. The magic Chart shows you where to look, and the Guided Association sessions show you how to empty out your past sorrows. When you have done this, you will be able to look squarely in the face of the past, no matter what happened. And you will laugh in its face, or even be bored to think that such nonsense ever ruled and ruined your health.

Your conflict check chart

By means of this list you will review the major causes of conflict in your entire lifetime. These times of worry, fear, grief, rage, loss, tragedy, pain, and the like, are the roots of your present psychosomatic health-wreckers.

Get your pen or pencil and *start checking now.*

INFANCY AND CHILHOOD	Yes	No
1. Excessive coddling		
2. Excessive affection, with every whim gratified		
3. Discouraged initiative		
4. Strict regimentation		
5. Strict toilet-training		
6. Strict religious training...................		

Yes   No

7. A strong sense of sin and guilt................
8. Demanding, possessive parents..............
9. Parents discussed illness and other problems in your presence ....
10. Constant wrangling and arguments between parents ....
11. Constant conflict as to which parent was to be obeyed ....
12. Setting other children on a pedestal as an example to you..............................
13. Overdiscipline, with no choice of conduct offered to you.............................
14. Discipline by fear and punishment
    a. physical ....
    b. emotional—threat of sin.................
15. Teaching that sex is sinful...................
16. Lack of information, poor information, or misinformation on sex........................
17. Parents stayed together for your sake.........
18. Were you an only child?....................
    a. Coddled ....
    b. No competition ....
    c. No self-reliance ....
    d. Never learned to share with others.........
    e. Remained attached to mother or father to an unusual degree ....
19. Envy of a second child.....................
    a. Were you made to feel less important when the other child arrived?..................
    b. Was the competition too difficult?.........
20. Were you an unwanted child?...............

ADOLESCENCE

1. Overcritical parents ....
2. Parents posed as paragons of virtue.........
3. Did you think of your parents as paragons of virtue, and were you later disillusioned?......
4. No free choice of opinion and course of action..

5. Overdiscipline ....
6. Pretended or actual illness of parent to hold you
   close to home...............................
7. Unpleasant home atmosphere.................
   a. Constant bickering ....
   b. Pessimistic parents ....
   c. Lack of economic security..................
   d. Marital incompatibility ....
   e. Unsatisfactory neighborhood ....
8. Were you ridiculed during awkward age of
   adolescence and made to feel self-conscious or
   inferior? ....
9. Rigid religious instruction....................
10. No sex instruction...........................
11. Street corner sex instruction.................
12. Sex instruction by obscene literature.........
13. Unsatisfactory sex experience with your own sex
14. Unsatsfactory sex experiences with the opposite
    sex ....
15. False modesty with regard to sex.............
    a. Demonstrated by parents ....
    b. Demonstrated by teachers ....
    c. Demonstrated by religious leaders ....
    d. Demonstrated by companions ....
16. Attitude toward masturbation
    a. Told that it was normal...................
    b. Told that it was a sin....................
    c. Told that it would lead to mental deteriora-
       tion ....
    d. Told that it would lead to physical deteriora-
       tion ....

ADULT LIFE

1. Marital Problems
   a. Was your marriage an escape from an un-
      satisfactory home environment?...........
   b. Did you marry for money?................
   c. Did you marry because of puppy love?.....

Yes   No

    d. Was your love entirely physical?..........

    e. Is there nothing in common with your mate?
       Intellectually? ....
       Emotionally? ....
       Spiritually? ....

    f. Did your family force the marriage?.......

2. Are you bored with your mate?..............

3. Do you constantly seek escape from home?....
    a. Lodges ....
    b. Other social activities.....................
    c. Out with the boys (or girls)..............
    d. Bars and Grills..........................
    e. Nightclubs, and so forth..................

4. Sex needs unsatisfied.......................

5. Inability to satisfy sex needs of your partner or
    vice versa ....

6. Your temperaments differ...................
    a. You are optimistic and your partner is pessi-
       mistic ....
    b. You like the company of others and your part-
       ner prefers to be alone...................
    c. You need affection and your partner is in-
       different ....

7. Your mental level is higher or lower than part-
    ner's ....

8. Your religious beliefs are different from partner's

9. You have a child and there is a question as to
    what the religious training should be.........

10. Your ideas on training your child in all respects
    differ from those of your partner.............

11. You have no children and don't want any, but
    your partner does (or vice versa)............

12. You don't feel a need for your mate...........

13. Your mate feels no need for you..............

14. You have no common interests either in his busi-
    ness or elsewhere.........................

15. You do not enjoy sharing your experiences and
    activities ....

16. Your in-laws are troublesome..............
17. There are financial difficulties..............
18. Sudden wealth led to a change in attitude.....
19. You know nothing of the anatomy of sex......
20. You know nothing of the sex functions.......
21. Your partner knows nothing of sex anatomy or functions ....
22. You do not enjoy the sex act................
23. Your partner does not enjoy the sex act.......
24. You indulge in it merely for the satisfaction of your partner ....
25. You pretend to enjoy it, but you do not have an orgasm ....
26. All that you know about sex you learned at bridge parties or from friends..............
27. The sex act gives you a feeling of guilt........
    a. due to misinformation...................
    b. due to strict religious training............
    c. sex is a sin..........................
28. You believe that you are frigid and that your partner is impotent......................
29. Your husband ejaculates prematurely before you get any satisfaction......................
30. You have consulted a physician for sex instruction ....
31. Your partner has consulted a physician for sex instruction ....
32. You fear pregnancy......................
33. You fear venereal disease..................
34. You feel that your partner has been promiscuous
35. You feel that your partner is dissatisfied with you sexually ....
36. You are dissatisfied with your partner sexually
37. Your partner is not physically clean.........
38. You are not physically clean................
39. There is insufficient byplay in the sex act.....
40. You are always tired when the sex act is performed ....

Yes   No

41. Sexual intercourse is always associated with argument or nagging......................
42. You feel that the sexual demands of your partner are perversions ....
43. You have a physical defect that bothers you....
    a. Large ears ....
    b. Large or unattractive nose................
    c. Receding chin ....
    d. Pendulous breasts ....
    e. Other defects ....
44. You have been rejected in love...............
45. The death of a parent plunged you into despair
46. You lost money..........................
47. You lost your job........................
48. You did not receive the advance you expected..
49. Your children are not developing as you feel they should ....
50. You have more troubles than anyone..........
51. Your recent worries are to be listed here.......

    ....

    ....

    ....

52. Your mate is losing interest in you and this illness is an opportunity to keep him (her) at home ....
53. Someone else is more attractive to your mate and your illness will hold him (her)........
54. Your illness prevents your child from leaving home, and that is just what you want........
55. Your illness makes it hard on some member of your family, and you'd like to revenge yourself on that person.........................
56. You find it hard to get a job, and your illness offers an easy explanation................
57. You like to have someone else support you....

Now that you have filled in the Conflict Check Chart, go back over it and see if you have been completely honest. If you feel that there should be any changes made, make them now.

The Conflict Check Chart is your first step to better health. When you fill it out, you are discovering the roots of your psychosomatic symptoms, the source of your health-wreckers.

Recognize your behavior patterns

You can now recognize your behavior pattern. You can begin to see the answers to the important questions: 1. How mature am I? 2. Am I a child in an adult's body? 3. Is unanswered organ language destroying my health?

It is often a good idea, if you are so inclined, to outline or write a brief autobiography, the story of your life. Keep it simple. This will be very helpful when used together with the Conflict Check Chart. The two together will provide leads for Guided Association that could not be found by either method alone. In the next chapter you will learn how to use Guided Association to follow up on these leads and to rid yourself of your psychosomatic health problems.

You will find behavior patterns that you never suspected. Most often they will be related to the personality development patterns you have already learned about. *Key words* will also be helpful to you in bringing back your earliest painful memories.

The key words of your past

Your past is different from mine only in its specifics. The general development patterns are quite similar. This is true of all of us, and it is because of these basic, general development patterns of the past that we can relatively easily reach back into our past and unearth the problem spots.

For example, we all had problems with our parents. It is safe to say that we all hated our parents at one time or another. That is not to say that we might not have loved them most of the time, but we certainly did not see eye to eye all the time. And there were times when you wished they were dead. For that matter—hold on to your hats—there were times when they wished we were dead, or at least that we had never been born.

The important point is that you need have no guilt about the fact that your love for your parents was not constant. You need not feel guilty if you hated them. And you need not feel neglected or despised if they disliked or even hated you. No one can stay

at a constant pitch of any emotion 24 hours of every day, day
after day. Sometimes we love, and sometimes we hate the same
person we loved. This is normal, and need not distress you. Look
back into your past and recall the times you hated your parents
and the times they treated you badly. They might have been stern
"for your own good" and punished you with the "it hurts me
more than it hurts you," and "I am saving your soul" expressions.
When you understand their behaviour better, and your own
mixed feelings of love and hate toward them, you will perhaps
learn to laugh at the repressed "violence" in your mind's Silent
Level.

And so we come to the Key Words of your past, words you
will use in a very specific way when you practice Guided Association. These are very important words, for they will help you
reach into your past to get rid of the emotionally charged times
of trouble, worry, pain, and grief—times that have been seething
in your subconscious mind and erupting as your psychosomatic
health-wreckers.

For example, were your parents cold or overindulgent? Either
way, what do you do now—as an adult—that is still a rebellion
against your parents? The Key Word is obviously *Parents,* or
perhaps, *Mom, Mother, Dad, Father* or *Pop.* When you practice
your daily Guided Association treatment, each of these Key Words
will help you reach back into your childhood. You will then write
down the disturbing thoughts and times that come flooding back
into your mind when you read or speak these words. These Key
Words and others will help you release the pus-laden, symptom-
producing, repressed memories of your emotions at the Silent
Level.

A key word list

Use the following list to help you get the most out of your
Conflict Check Chart and your written, outlined, life story. Use
these words to reactivate painful childhood memories, troubled
adolescent experiences, times of actual pain and distress, tears
and rage, violence and crime, frustration and unrequited love—in
short, all times of emotional disturbances that have been partially or completely repressed. These are the times and the
experiences that may be causing or aggravating your psychoso-

matic health-wreckers. (The next chapter will show you exactly
how to use this list.)

> Your pet names for your parents:
> Mother—*Mom, Ma.*
> Father—*Dad, Pop, Pa, Governor.*
> Your parents' pet names for you:————————.
> The names of your pets, especially if you lost them through
> death or violence:————————.
> Your special names for:
> Brother————————, Sister————————.
> Their special names for you:————————.
> Your names for: sex————————, stool or bowel movement
> ————————.
> The names of all sex organs, especially your nicknames for
> them:————————.
> Your special names for sexual intercourse:————————.
> Your own terms for:

> | Kiss | Breast | Nipple | Thumb | Food |
> |-------|---------|--------|-------|------|
> | Death | Funeral | Hate | Love | Kill |

The key words of organ language

Organ Language is a language of *feelings* and *symptoms.*
There are no words in this language, and so it is a language that
more closely approximates reality. Words are not the reality they
represent, as you know; but the feelings and symptoms of organ
language are true reality.

Nothing is more "real" to the sufferer than a cramp in the
stomach, a painful spasm of the "gut," a feeling of nausea, vomiting, diarrhea or constipation, headache, migraine, chest pain, the
pain of heart artery spasm or closure, the pitiful wheeze of
asthma, the unmanageable sneezing of hay fever, and all the
other innumerable symptoms of body-mind disorders.

And so the key words of organ language are not words at
all. They are the reality of the way we feel when we are sick.

Still, there are words that have found their way into our everyday language, words that express the way our disturbed organs feel. You may use these key words that represent organ language to reactivate unpleasant memories to round out your Conflict Check Chart and autobiography, and, later, for your Guided Association sessions.

Headache	Spineless
Heartache	Guts
Shaky	Gripe
All-gone	Vomit
Weak all over	Nausea
Swallow	

(Please go back and consult the organ language phrases of Chapter 3 for more of this important material.)

It is obvious that this word list, and even the organ language phrases of our everyday speech, are only pale approximations of the reality of our symptoms and feelings. But they will suffice to bring back the times of illness or emotional distress we are now seeking. They will help to round out the search started in the Conflict Check Chart.

And now I want to show you, in a step-by-step way, how to apply all that you have learned to this point to get rid of your emotion-based symptoms, your psychosomatic health-wreckers. We will do this by means of a representative case history.

How John R. detected and conquered his psychosomatic problem

In reading this story, remember that *the method is the important thing,* and not the particular symptoms of this patient. Your own symptoms may be very different, but the method of treatment is the one you will use.

John R. was a very unhappy automobile mechanic, and his wife was a school teacher in a grade school. His income was moderate, his debts were many, and his outlook was that of a deepening depression. He could see no future for himself, and he derived less and less pleasure from his work. He suffered severe headaches, heartburn, and backaches. He carried stomach-soothing medicines and aspirin with him all the time.

I examined him carefully, and found only a slight heart murmur (and said nothing about it), small internal "piles" that bled occasionally, and nothing else. His palms were very moist and his hands trembled slightly—common evidence of a sensitive nervous system and anxiety.

His history showed that his father had died at a relatively early age of a heart attack. His mother died of cancer of the brain, and had suffered severe headaches for two years before she died. One of his brothers, seven years older than John, had been in and out of a mental institution with a "split personality" problem. His grandparents, he thought, had heart disease on both sides of the family.

The importance of this family history is obvious. It shows us what John might be worrying about, even though he might not realize it at the time. It provides John with leads to use in filling out his Conflict Check Chart and in practicing his Guided Association. You will do the same.

STEP ONE

Prepare a brief story of your life and a short outline of your family tree. List all the diseases and causes of death as far back as you can.

You may be surprised to find that all or many of your present symptoms are due to your conscious or unconscious identification with your mother, your father, a brother or sister, or with your grandparents. It is natural for you to worry about the family diseases and causes of death and to think that the same things could happen to you.

If several members of your family died of cancer, it is normal for you to fear cancer. And this fear may cause symptoms and depression—psychosomatic health-wreckers in any part of your body.

John said he had "three family disease strikes against him." He was sure that he was doomed to die from heart disease, cancer of the brain, or from a complete mental breakdown. The source of his fear was obvious.

STEP TWO

Fill out your Conflict Check Chart. You must face your fears and bring them to the surface. That is the purpose of your brief life story and family disease history, and the purpose of the Conflict Check Chart. *Repressed fears are deadly.* They cause your symptoms. Faced fears can be overcome.

When you fill out your Conflict Check Chart you face your fears, your guilt, the emotional trials and tribulations of your entire lifetime.

STEP THREE

Explanation and reassurance are the essence of this step. John was given all the facts. We discussed his family history and the very natural fears he had. I pointed out to him, as I now point out to you, that every person living has a set of fears very much like his own. These fears are based upon family disease and how loved ones died, and are compounded by overexposure to advertising and educational campaigns of the various societies for the prevention of cancer, heart disease, and mental and nervous system disease. We are all bombarded by such propaganda, and although it serves a good educational purpose, it also destroys our peace of mind and makes hypochondriacs of us all.

It is important for you to understand that you do not stand alone in your fears, no matter what they are. You are just like the rest of us, fearing failure and death. Be reassured that with the help of your family doctor and the simple methods of this book, you can bring your psychosomatic symptoms under control. You can improve your health. You can even lengthen your life. You have already started on that path, and the next chapters of this book will lead you, step-by-step, to the better health you now seek.

STEP FOUR

Guided Association comes next. You will be doing this in the privacy of your own home, and the next chapter tells you how. Guided Association helped John get rid of his worries, the guilt and fears of his earlier life, and his repressed and unrecognized emotional dynamite. His headaches cleared completely. Soon his heartburn came under control, and he threw away his stomach medicines. His backaches became less annoying, and he could get under cars without difficulty.

Guided Association will help you do the same with your psychosomatic symptoms.

And finally, if you have any body changes, as John did, your family doctor will correct them. For example, I used injection treatment (a painless office method) to shrink down John's piles and stop the bleeding. I put him on a special diet to safeguard his heart. (Turn to Chapter 8 for the details of this diet and the Cantor Cocktail to lower blood cholesterol and help prevent heart disease.)

The lessons of the John R. case

This typical case gives you the FOUR-STEP METHOD to rid yourself of psychosomatic health-wrecker symptoms:

1. Outline your life story and family history of disease and causes of death. Stress your fears, especially your health and death fears.
2. Complete your Conflict Check Chart, looking for times of worry, stress, injury, tears, grief, violence, and all other emotional disturbances from your birth to the present moment. Use the general and organ language Key Word lists to help you recall your troubled past.
3. See your physician if you have not already done so and be carefully examined by him. Ask for an explanation of your problem and for reassurance if no serious changes are found in your body.

    Be reassured, for you are not alone in having such symptoms and worries. We all have them.
4. Now read the next chapter, and practice the methods of Guided Association, Self-Suggestion, and Relaxation every day of your life. You will probably get rid of your symptoms quickly, and you will then continue to use these methods to prevent future troubles.

Points to remember:

1. See your family physician first.
2. After a complete physical examination and laboratory studies, discuss the problem with him.
3. If there are no serious organ or tissue changes, you may begin self-treatment of your psychosomatic health-wreckers.

4. If organ or tissue changes are found, start medically controlled treatment or surgery as ordered.
5. The Conflict Check Chart will pinpoint the stress areas of your lifetime, especially when used with the autobiography outline and the Key Words.
6. Psychosomatic self-therapy will be useful to control your underlying emotional stress, even if you do have organic body changes. This therapy will help you to heal better, faster, and with less emotional strain.

Chapter 5

HOW TO TREAT YOUR ANXIETY PROBLEMS

How to use chapter 5

We will now continue to work together, hand in hand, for the relief of your psychosomatic symptoms.

I assume that you have already outlined your life story and family history of disease and causes of death, with special stress on your fears; and, likewise, that you have filled out your personal Conflict Check Chart. If you have not done this, DO IT NOW.

When this is done, you will be ready for the next step, and we will work together, right in your own home. This is what you do:

1. Read this chapter and in it I will tell you about Persuasion, Explanation, and Reassurance.

2. Self-suggestion is the next step. This is the major key to personality reconstruction, self-mastery, and the release from your psychosomatic symptoms. Practice these methods exactly as suggested. You will find them easy, and you will weave them into your daily pattern of living.

Step-by-step I will teach you how to relax instantly, sleep instantly, control pain instantly, release yourself from fear and worry instantly.

3. You are now ready to begin the amazing Guided Association sessions. Again, I will guide you, and you will see exactly how to do this right in your own home.

You will release yourself from the distress, pain, guilt and shame—all the worries of your past. As you do this, your psychosomatic symptoms will gradually vanish, and you will become happier and healthier with each passing day.

4. I will then tell you how to use Substitute Aggression Release therapy, in your own home, on the golf course—every day of your life. This simple method will rid you of repressed violence in a rapid and harmless way. The inner tensions associated with such violence will melt away. With them will go such symptoms as headache, heartache, and other related psychosomatic problems.

You must remember that you are now learning a way of life, methods that you will use every day to become healthier and to stay healthy. You will want to refer back to this chapter at frequent intervals from now on. You will use the methods of this chapter and this book every day.

The major therapy of your anxiety problems rests with you. The instructions you will receive in this book and the guidance you may obtain from your physician can only set you on the right path. But it is you, and you alone, who must develop the new patterns of thought and living that will lead you down the path to good health and long life. And so we come to the important realization that, although you must cooperate with your physician, you must go even further and practice the treatment methods to be revealed in this chapter and throughout this book. Practice them until they become second nature to you. Practice until they alter your thinking patterns, your attitudes, your emotions, and even your basic physiology.

In this chapter you will actually learn how to control your body functions. You will learn the methods of the physician, explanation and reassurance, and what they will do for you. You will learn about his careful study to rule out basic organic pathology and the importance of this study to you. You will come to realize the true meaning of *psychosomatic* in the practical application of combined treatment of body and mind as a single unit.

You will learn also the amazing self-suggestion techniques for the control of otherwise uncontrollable body functions. You will become expert in the application of these methods for the deep relaxation of your entire body. The combination of these two forms of therapy—deep relaxation and self-suggestion—is most important, and you will learn how to achieve this combination in actual practice, in your own home.

Then you will go on to the Guided Association and Emotional

Release therapy, methods that may save you many years on the analyst's couch. You will become informed in the differences between the Free Association method of Freud and my own Guided Association method.

Finally, you will learn the all-important method of combining deep relaxation, self-suggestion and its Key Words, and Guided Association for the control of the all-important body-mind unit. It is this control, *control by yourself*, that is an important element in eliminating psychosomatic symptoms.*

You and your doctor

It is obviously most important not to attempt self-diagnosis. Such efforts may cost you your life. See your physician first. After he has made a careful study of your general physical condition and performed the necessary laboratory tests, discuss your problem with him. If there are underlying organic changes that require medical treatments, drugs or surgery, these must be attended to without undue delay. If he assures you that your condition is emotional in origin, or is being aggravated by emotional reactions, you may then apply the methods of this book to hasten your recovery. Even if the condition is organic, there is always an emotional component that requires attention. This emotional factor will respond best to the forms of self-treatment you are about to learn.

Explanation and reassurance

After your physician has completed his studies, he will provide a full explanation of your condition as revealed by those studies. However, you must not expect your physician to be a specialist in every field. He cannot possibly encompass the full range of modern medicine. No one can. It is enormous, and growing more complex every day. But he can and will provide you with his best opinions and with his most accurate diagnosis. Once you know the extent of the organic component of your problems, you can bring that under control with your physician's guidance. Most physicians do not have the time, inclination, or training to go beyond this point into the realm of psychotherapy. It is here

_____

* See my book, UNITROL: *The Healing Magic of the Mind,* Parker Publishing Company, © 1965.

that you can help your physician and yourself by applying the methods you are about to learn.

The first step, then, is the explanation by your physician, and, we hope, his reassurance that your condition is curable. He may tell you that your problem is entirely emotion-based. Or, he may find that the emotions are the major element but that there are also organic changes to be treated. Or, there may be an important organic factor, and a lesser emotional problem. Please remember that there is always a combination of body and emotions in every medical problem. It is impossible to separate the two. It is the body-mind unit that is to be treated, and that is the true meaning of the word *psychosomatic*.

Persuasion

It may seem odd to think that persuasion is an important element of therapy, but it is. You would be amazed to know that many patients are so convinced that they have cancer that it is very difficult to persuade them that they are free of this disease. I remember Mr. John S. quite well indeed, for he presented this very problem. His complaints had to do with the large bowel. He had severe constipation, and bleeding with bowel movement. His best friend had just died of cancer of the rectum. He was convinced that he himself had this dread disease. Despite careful examination, including X-ray studies and sigmoidoscopy (looking into the lower bowel through a lighted instrument), he could not be persuaded that his condition was merely a matter of poor bowel training, emotional spasm of the large bowel, and bleeding, internal hemorrhoids. I removed his hemorrhoids in my office, using my own methods and instruments for painless, bloodless rectal surgery, and he drove his own car home immediately after the procedure. He was back at his desk the next day.

The bleeding was now under control, and the next problem was the correction of the constipation. This required retraining of his bowel habits, a change in diet, and continual reassurance that his condition was not cancer. He continued to think only of cancer and equated his condition with his late friend's symptoms and death. This ultimately called for Guided Association Therapy, and training in deep relaxation. It was only after a year of such combined therapy, and repeated X-ray studies, that he was finally

convinced that his condition was not malignant, and that he was
not about to die.

Self-suggestion therapy

Self-suggestion is one of the major keys to personality reconstruction. When you learn to apply this method to your emotion-
based problems you will be able to do unbelievable things. You
will learn to relax instantly on command from yourself. You will
learn to make any part of your body numb for the relief of pain
or in anticipation of discomfort. You will learn how to change
your habits of thinking, your attitudes, and your feelings in a
rapid and permanent way. You will learn how to replace your
childish and immature habits with mature, adult ways of thinking and behavior. All this sounds unbelievable, but you will soon
learn the simple methods of self-suggestion that make it possible.

Relaxation—The first step in self-suggestion

You will now begin your training in self-suggestion, taking
the important first step of learning how to relax your muscles and
mind. The easiest time to relax, of course, is at bedtime. That is
the time when you normally let your muscles go limp and loose,
let your mind go blank, and fall to sleep. That is your goal, to attain this deeply relaxed state of mind and body *instantly*.

You can do this at any time of the day, as you will soon learn.
For the first step, however, you will start with the easiest method
and use self-suggestion just before falling asleep.

Imagine you are lying in your bed, on your back. Your arms
are lying alongside your body. You are breathing slowly and
shallowly. Every muscle in your body is limp and loose. You feel
warm and at peace. Your mind is stilled and ready for sleep. You
are less and less aware of your body. Your brain is now ready to
turn itself off and go to sleep.

But what if you are so tense and anxious when you are ready
for bed that you toss and turn, your body given over to purposeless
activity, your mind to anxious, rapid-fire thoughts, your muscles
tense and active? Your first step is to learn the feeling of a tense
muscle, and then to learn the wonderful, soothing relief and rest
of a relaxed muscle. You do this in the same position, lying flat
on your back, arms lying at your sides. Now clench your fists—a

sign of anger, fear, anxiety, fight. Feel the tension in the muscles of your hands and forearm. Learn to recognize the feel of a tense, anxious muscle. This is the sensation you want to eliminate and replace. Now, relax your fists and let your hands lie limp and loose. That is the feeling of relaxed muscles, the sensation of peace and harmony you will soon enjoy in every part of your body. When you learn to experience this sensation of relaxed muscles throughout your body, all tension and anxiety will ooze away, you will be fully relaxed, and you will sleep peacefully.

Now tense the muscles of your forearms and wrists by bending your wrists forcefully upwards toward your head, keeping your arms at your sides. Then let your hands fall back to the bed, relaxing the wrists and the forearm muscles. Feel the tension disappear?

Now flex your arms so that your elbows bend and your hands touch your shoulders, in the "make a muscle" position. Feel the tense, tight muscles in your upper arms? Now let your arms fall limp and loose at your sides. Feel the tension disappear, the muscles relax?

Let your mind start with your toes, and see for yourself whether or not this sensation of tense muscles is there in your toes, your feet, your legs, your thighs, your abdomen, your chest, your shoulders, your arms and forearms and hands, and finally your cheeks, forehead, scalp, and eyes.

Now that you know how a tight, anxious muscle feels, and how it feels when relaxed, you can check each set of muscles as your mind moves from toes to scalp. If there is tension in any set of muscles, tell them to relax.

Your muscles will do whatever you tell them to do

This is the key—the muscles are yours, your servants, and they will do whatever you tell them to do. If you allow them to get the upper hand, to become your master, then they will tell you what to do. They will go tense, and you will become anxious, restless, ill at ease, and jittery. Don't let them do this to you. You are the master. The muscles are yours, under your control, and you need only realize this and act accordingly. They will do exactly what you tell them to do. Remember the key—YOU TELL THEM. Don't let them tell you. THEY WILL DO WHATEVER YOU TELL

THEM TO DO. Tell them to relax, to go limp and loose. They will do exactly that, and your whole body will soon feel as if it were floating in air. It will be as if you were floating in space with no body at all.

How to switch off your brain

And now I want you to learn another secret of relaxation, another important key to self-control. When you think, you think in words, and the muscles of your vocal cords and throat, and perhaps even your mouth, move slightly as your mind forms words and thoughts. In other words, even your thoughts are keyed to muscle movements. This is of enormous importance. Once you learn to fully relax the muscles of your throat and mouth and lips, thinking will automatically stop, your mind will go blank, and you will be able to fall asleep instantly. See how important it is to learn to relax all body muscles!

Think of the brain as having a switch in it, a switch that you can throw to the "Off" position, or a button that you can push to turn off all brain activity. Throw that switch, push that button, and let your brain go to sleep.

Another simple method is to think of a single black dot on a gray page, and watch the dot spread (in your mind's eye) to cover the whole page. When the page is entirely black, you will be fully relaxed and your brain will be asleep.

Or use the repetitive self-suggestion, saying to yourself over and over again, slowly and then rapidly, *sleep, sleep, sleep, sleep, sleep,* . . . until you are fully relaxed and drop off into a deep, restful sleep.

The best time for self-suggestion

Bedtime, when you are ready to fall to sleep, is the best time to implant suggestions in your subconscious mind. It is the time when your subconscious mind is most receptive, the time when your suggestions will be acted upon without question. For example, if you have been overeating, this is the time to tell yourself: *I will never feel hungry. I have no desire for the foods not allowed. From now on I will eat smaller and smaller portions. Every day, in every way, I am becoming slimmer and slimmer, younger and younger, healthier and healthier.* This slimming, rejuvenating self-suggestion, implanted in your subconscious mind during this state of deep relaxation, is accepted and acted upon throughout the night and every day thereafter. Your body knows what to do to accomplish its mission, and the implanted self-suggestion need merely set the destination.

You can do the same with self-suggestions for happiness, better health, character changes, and so forth. For example:

Every day, in every way, I am becoming happier and happier.

or,

Every cell, every tissue, every organ, every part of my body is becoming healthier and healthier, younger and younger, every day, in every way.

This is an excellent, all-purpose self-suggestion to improve your general health and sense of well-being. You can safely leave this suggestion in your subconscious mind at bedtime each night. Your body will act upon it as if it were a command and will deploy the necessary body resources to accomplish your orders.

The relaxation formula for the beginner

1. Practice relaxation just before going to sleep, while lying down.
2. Then, when you have learned how to achieve full relaxation in the reclining position, practice relaxation while sitting up, during the day.
3. Use post-relaxation suggestions to control your body-mind unit throughout the day. These are very effective, exactly like the self-suggestions you give to the subconscious mind just before falling off to sleep.

Let me guide you now through a full relaxation session. You may use the following words or your own, as you choose. The important thing is to grasp the idea, then you can put it into your own words as you talk to, and control, your subconscious mind. Since you already have some experience with the method of relaxation while lying down, I will teach you the sitting relaxation technique at this time. You can practice this in your own home, at the movies or at a play, or even while at work. If you relax while at the theatre or at work, you will naturally relax from the neck down, allowing your head and mind to remain awake and alert. I do this at the theatre regularly, and go into a very deep state of relaxation while enjoying the show. You will soon learn to do the same, and will experience the wonderful satisfaction of a fully relaxed body combined with an alert mind. For the present, however, we want to learn the technique of deep relaxation of the entire body.

Sit down and relax

Sit in a chair you find both comfortable and relaxing. Rest your feet on the floor, let your hands rest upon your lap, palms downward on your thighs. Be certain that the room will remain quiet, and that you will not be disturbed by the telephone or by visitors. Loosen your clothing.

Now, close your eyes and let your head drop forward as if you were nodding in sleep. Let your eyes close in a relaxed fashion. Just let the eyelids become heavier and heavier, so that they fall downward of their own weight.

Now, let your cheeks go limp and loose. Let your forehead become smooth as your mouth drops slightly open.

Your head is now touching your chest, and you are breathing slowly and deeply. With each breath, every muscle in your body is becoming looser and looser, more and more relaxed. You are now limp and loose, like a fully relaxed cat curled before a fireplace, fast asleep.

Feel the pleasant warmth and heaviness throughout your body. You have a deep sense of calm and peace and quiet. You are on the verge of sleep.

Now you take over

Now we are about to transfer control to you, and you will allow your conscious mind to talk to your subconscious mind as follows:

My feet and legs are completely relaxed and asleep.
My thighs are asleep.
My hands, arms, forearms, and shoulders are completely relaxed and asleep.
My entire body, from the neck down, is completely relaxed and asleep.

I feel a wonderful peace and warmth throughout my entire body.

I am now in a deep state of relaxation—deeper and deeper with each breath.

My forehead is relaxed, my eyes are relaxed, my cheeks are relaxed.

Every cell, every tissue, every organ of my body is now completely relaxed, at ease, asleep.

I am now completely receptive to all health-building suggestions. These health-building suggestions will work within and for me all day and all night, every day, to make me stronger and stronger, happier and happier, healthier and healthier. They will work within and for me when my body wakes, and at all times thereafter, awake and asleep.

A note for those who know self-hypnosis

Those of my readers who are acquainted with the methods of hypnosis (especially those who have read the excellent book by LeCron, *Self Hypnosis: The Technique and Its Use in Daily Living*) will recognize that this method of deep relaxation and self-suggestion produces exactly the same effect as self-hypnosis. In my opinion, however, this technique is superior to both hypnosis and self-hypnosis since it requires no one other than the reader to produce its effects and does so while awake and asleep, all day, every day. Nevertheless, I suggest that the reader would do well to obtain the LeCron book as well, and familiarize himself with its methods.

Now use self-suggestion

When you have attained this state of deep relaxation, while sitting or lying down, at home, at work or in the theatre, your subconscious is fully prepared to receive, accept, and put into effect any health-building self-suggestions you may offer. It will accept these suggestions without question, will treat them as commands, and they will work to improve your health and your personality from that time on.

Do you want to lose weight? Use this self-suggestion:

Every day, in every way, I am becoming slimmer and slimmer. I enjoy my new diet, and I want only the foods allowed. I have no desire to eat between meals.

Do you want to control pain? Place your hand on the painful area, and repeat the following as rapidly and continuously as you can:

The pain is going, going, going, going, going . . . Continue to repeat the word *going* indefinitely until the pain is entirely gone. Another excellent word to replace the word *going* is the word *better. The pain is better, better, better, better.* . . .

Or you can actually anesthetize the painful area by placing your hand over it and repeating the following self-suggestion:

All sensation is leaving, and I am becoming more and more numb. Soon there will be complete anesthesia under my hand.

As you practice these methods, you will develop great skill and effectiveness. Your suggestibility will increase each time you try and, before long, you will be able to produce *instant sleep* to correct insomnia, *instant anesthesia* to relieve pain, *instant control* of excessive appetite to fight obesity, and *instant peace and contentment* to combat anxiety.

This is one of the most valuable skills you will ever acquire. If you accomplish nothing else in your entire lifetime, self-control will be yours in consequence of this self-suggestion relaxation method. The Bible and the ancient scriptures of the Orient teach that the man who conquers himself is a greater conqueror than the general who conquers a city. You now have it in your power to accomplish this wondrous feat.

Key word magic for instant action

You are now ready to learn the rapid and reinforcement methods of self-suggestion. When you have become proficient in the relaxation technique, and have practiced self-suggestion for a time, you may take this giant step to the rapid or Key Word Method. Usually, you will need one to four weeks of practice in the methods described above before starting on this advanced technique.

Let us assume that you are now ready. In this method you use only the Key Words, the words that represent the entire pattern of thought to be transmitted to your subconscious mind for immediate, delayed, or continuous action.

We will start with the Key Word Method to produce instant

and complete, deep relaxation. The natural key word is simply *relax*. When you are already in a deep state of relaxation, produced as formerly described, give the following self-suggestion to your subconscious mind:

From this time on, when I wish to attain the present state of deep relaxation, I will be instantly and fully relaxed, just as I now am, the moment I say "relax." This word will have this effect only when I say it, and only under the proper circumstances, when I am ready to receive healing self-suggestions. From this point on, and under these circumstances, the word relax *will mean the following:*

My entire body, from the neck down, is completely relaxed and asleep. I feel wonderful, deeply relaxed, a wonderful peace and quiet throughout my entire body.

I am now completely receptive to all healing and life-prolonging suggestions. My subconscious will direct every cell, every tissue, every organ of my body to put these healing and life-prolonging commands into effect without delay, and they will act within me all through the day and night, every day.

To produce instant sleep

If you wish to produce instant Key Word sleep, you may tell your subconscious mind that the Key Word phrase for instant sleep will be *relax and sleep*. You will instantly go into a deep state of relaxation and a deep, restful, refreshing sleep. This is a wonderful treatment for the correction of insomnia. This is an excellent way to end any self-suggestion session when you are practicing at bedtime. Be certain to tell yourself how many hours you wish to sleep, and your subconscious mind will act as an effective alarm clock the next morning. And tell yourself that when you wake you will feel wonderful, alert, alive, vigorous, full of good health and energy. You may also wish to tell your subconscious mind to start the necessary internal forces at work to make you younger and younger, happier and happier, healthier and healthier while you sleep. Your body will do just that in response to this self-suggestion, working throughout the night to accomplish its mission. You don't need to provide detailed instructions. Your subconscious mind unerringly provides the necessary mechanisms for you.

How to reinforce your self-suggestions

Once you have become expert in the rapid Key Word Method for the production of deep relaxation and self-suggestion, you may proceed to use the following suggestion for *reinforcement:*

From now on, each command that I give to the subconscious mind will become more and more effective, will act 24 hours a day, and will become stronger and stronger, more and more effective with each passing day.

Use this reinforcement self-suggestion when you are deeply relaxed and receptive.

To activate the effects of the commands, even while awake, and without any preliminary relaxation, use the following self-suggestion while in a deep state of relaxation:

From now on, every time I issue a health-giving command to my subconscious mind, even while awake, it will take instant effect, and will make me healthier and healthier, stronger and stronger, younger and younger, happier and happier.

The reinforcement technique, especially in the form that is effective even while awake and without preceding deep relaxation, is very valuable and should be practiced each day from now on. Once you have established this self-suggestion in your subconscious mind during the state of deep relaxation and receptivity, you may proceed to issue commands of a positive, healthful nature directly to your subconscious mind at any time of the day or night.

If you find yourself depressed, anxious, worried, ill at ease, or in any other negative state of mind, or in poor health, you need only issue a positive command to your subconscious mind to reverse that state of mind or body. Your subconscious mind will obey instantly to set in motion the necessary body forces to produce the required new conditions for improved health, happiness, strength, courage, etc. You will feel an actual surge of power throughout your body. The effect will be immediate, and you will experience a powerful sense of well-being. You can have instant peace of mind.

The ultimate waking suggestion

It is most important to use the following suggestion (in your own words if you wish) in any Self-Suggestion Relaxation Session that is to be followed by deep sleep. This suggestion will insure a sense of well-being and happiness throughout the day following your sleep session.

When I wake, I will feel wonderful. I will be younger, happier and healthier than I have ever been before. I will have perfect peace of mind. From this point on, throughout the day and night, and always, I will become younger and younger, happier and happier, healthier and healthier, every day, in every way.

Use this post-sleep, waking suggestion without fail. It ensures continuing action of your previous self-suggestions for improved health and happiness, no matter when you have given them to your subconscious mind.

How Free Association works

We will move on now to a brief discussion of the Free Association therapy of Freud, and a comparison of this method with my own Guided Association. I will then show you how to apply Guided Association in conjunction with the Conflict Check Chart and the Self-Suggestion methods. The result will give you full control of your body functions, to the degree to which you become proficient in this combination of methods.

Free Association is part of the method of psychoanalysis as described and practiced by Sigmund Freud. It has not changed since its first description by its founder and is practiced to this day by all psychoanalysts in its original form. Psychoanalysis is a psychology of the instincts, and it shows how our most important emotional behavior patterns begin in early childhood. It teaches that the ideas and emotions of our early life experiences are registered in our subconscious and act throughout our lifetime to influence our subsequent behavior.

The Free Association method of psychoanalysis, the heart of its therapy, requires that the patient lie down on a couch and simply talk freely and unrestrainedly, saying anything he may wish to say. The physician sits behind the couch, simply listening. He does not guide the direction of the patient's flow of language, nor its nature. In this relaxed atmosphere, the patient finds it easy to talk, at least after the first few sessions. Since he is instructed to say anything that may come into his mind, even if it seems inappropriate or irrelevant, feelings of hostility, fear, dependency, sexual fantasy, and the like will pour forth without restraint or censorship. The idea is for the patient to express gradually his total personality during the several sessions weekly throughout the one or more years of therapy.

Naturally, much truly irrelevant material pours forth during this year or more of treatment. In my opinion, the real release from repressed emotional dynamite, whether it originates in childhood or later in life, occurs during those times when the patient actually relives the disturbing experiences of his past. When this occurs in psychoanalysis free association, it is called *abreaction*. The mind gains considerable insight into its emotional problems at such times, and the result is good.

Those patients who can afford the expense and time required for this therapy, if they are under forty years of age, preferably unmarried, and not yet fixed in a career pattern, may benefit from psychoanalysis. The therapy is considered of relatively little value for those who are older, married, in a set career, or are parents— in other words, those already involved in irrevocable commitments to life. Further, this therapy is considered best for the fully developed neurosis, to prevent development of a psychosis, or to locate the cause of an unhappy personality maladjustment.

Since these conditions rule out most of us, and since there are not enough psychoanalysts to go around, even for those patients who qualify, it is important to find a quicker, easier, less expensive treatment. Besides all that, we are dealing in this book with the psychosomatic problem, and not with the fully developed neurotic or the psychotic. Even more important, most of us with psychosomatic problems are over forty, married, with children, and hard at work in our developing careers. And so I originated Guided Association and the Conflict Check Chart, to help the vast majority of sufferers from emotional disturbances, those with psychosomatic problems.

Guided Association

You are already familiar with the Conflict Check Chart (*See* Chapter 4). Turn to the Chart right now and review its contents. You will once again see that the chart leads you directly to the potentially disturbing areas at all stages of your development. If you have filled it out completely and honestly, you are now aware of your general problems. Certainly you are more aware of the location in your life patterns of your repressed emotional dynamite than you were before. This provides the guidance, the location finders, for the Guided Association therapy you are about to learn.

But you must first learn about the Silent Level, which is discussed below.

The Silent Level—*your emotional dynamite*

Conventional psychotherapy, as you have just seen, is mainly on the verbal level—talk, talk, talk, with only occasional points during which the patient actually relives the disturbing emotional experiences of his past. From where does he dredge up these emotional experiences? They are in his thalamus and hypothalamus, the emotion-carrying level of his brain structure. This pattern of emotionally charged, repressed dynamite, is called the Silent Level. Once it is released during Guided Association, it is far from silent. Since our repressed emotions are charged with anger, fear, despair, tears, threats, blows, violence of all kinds, there is apt to be shouting, crying, raging, and all forms of hostile or disturbed behavior as the emotional charge is set off during the Guided Association Therapy sessions.

And right there we have put our finger on the major point of difference between the rambling, verbal-level, free association treatment sessions, and the blowing off of steam, direct conflict approach of the Guided Association method. Guided Association, you see, goes directly to the areas of repressed dynamite in the Silent Level of your brain, and sets off the charge. It frees the repression energy for more useful constructive work. And that is why Guided Association is a more rapid, simpler, less expensive form of therapy. Indeed, it is a treatment you can put into effect right in your own home if you wish, with no more expense than the time and effort it calls for.

You can use Guided Association right now

Guided Association is easy to use. You will soon be able to reach into your subconscious Silent Level, the level of your emotions, and to release the repressed emotional dynamite of your past. The first step is the honest completion of the Conflict Check Chart.

Be certain to concentrate on the areas of painful emotion, grief, hostility, fear, anxiety—in a word, all stress situations throughout your lifetime. You may need to add a brief report on the following to the basic Conflict Check Chart.

1. All previous operations, illnesses, accidents.
2. The death of parents, children, relatives, friends, pets—anyone with whom you were emotionally bound.
3. The loss of money, business, job, confidence in your spouse.
4. Your nickname, the pet name your mother and father called you, and their pet expressions.
5. The relationship of your parents to each other, especially their quarrels, and their relationship to you.

We are particularly interested in locating the times of deep emotional reactions in your life pattern. Since you will be doing this in the privacy of your own home, you need have no fear of facing the emotional sore spots of your past, right down into your childhood. At this point you need only write them down in outline form, a simple 1,2,3 listing. These are the guide points for your Guided Association therapy. Stop a moment now, and realize that this simple step is the foundation, and major key to successful Guided Association therapy. Conceal nothing from yourself. *You have nothing to fear from the past, unless you hide from it.*

How to relive the past and release its emotions

The next step is to lie down in a quiet room at a time of day when you will not be disturbed. Be certain that you will not have to answer doorbells or telephones.

Now, use the simple relaxation techniques you have already learned and relax completely. Do not go to sleep, but do close your eyes.

Now go back in your mind to a time of great emotional stress, a time during which you cried with anguish and perhaps with fear. Let me give you an example to show you how this works in actual practice in the office. It works in exactly the same way at home, since you can guide yourself easily into the times of tears and trouble with the aid of your Conflict Check Chart.

I instruct the relaxed patient that he is to relive the disturbing episodes of his past in the present tense, exactly as if they were happening to him *right now*, and exactly as if he were the age at which they actually did occur. This is very important since part of our basic trouble is that we do not escape the past, and continue to relive it in our subconscious or conscious minds exactly as if we were still living in it. If the trouble spot occurred at six years of age, we continue to experience that event in our silent level brain areas just as if we were still six years of age. How silly it is to react at forty or fifty as we did when we were six, but that is exactly what we are all doing throughout our lives. Guided Association now brings this event to the surface with all its violent emotions. When you have discharged these emotions over and over again, you will realize how silly it is to continue to react to the past as if you were still living in it, how stupid it is for an adult to continue to behave like a child!

You have been listening to me instruct my patient who is lying on a couch or sitting on a chair in a state of complete relaxation. The patient now knows that he is to go back to an emotionally troubled time of his past, and that he is to relive that time as if it were happening right now, as if he were still the age at which it happened. He is then told to recount the episode in present tense, beginning with the statement, "I am now —— years old," giving me his age at the time of the event. He is then to describe every sight, every sound, every odor, every sensation he experienced at that time. He is to describe every person in the room, as well as the furniture and everything else in the room. He must *feel* himself in the room, with those people.

He must cry now if he cried then. He must speak whatever words he spoke at that time. He must hear every word he heard then. Most important of all, he must re-experience every emotion of that time.

I start the process, as you will start it at home, by using the information of the Check Chart.

"Your mother is dead. You are six years old. Tell me where you are, and everything that happens. Tell me who is here. Cry, if you cried then."

The patient may require frequent guidance to sights, sounds, odors, touch, or feelings, or he may move quickly into the past and relive the distress with great emotion. You must do the same during your private Guided Association sessions.

Please note that we are not interested in recalling the past merely as memory. This will do you some good, but not nearly as much as *true reliving* of the past as if it were occurring at the present moment.

The patient begins:

"I was in the room with my daddy," and I interrupt.

"I *am* in the room with my daddy. . . ." (You must *be there* *right now*. You *are* now six years old. It is happening *right now*.)

"I am in the room with my daddy, and he says to me, 'Son, I have bad news. Mommy is gone, and she won't come back. It isn't that she wanted to leave you, or that she didn't love you. She has been sick, and she just couldn't live any more.'

"Daddy is crying, and I cry too. I sit on his lap and I put my arms around him and I sob." (The patient cries desperately, like a child. He then goes on with the details of the scene, describing all that his father says to him and to the others in the room, and repeating, between sobs, all that he says to his father. He describes his father and the others, but especially his father. He describes everything in the room, as if he were in that room, *right now*.)

Repeated reliving is the key to permanent release from the past

Now we come to an important point. It is not enough to re-live this episode (or any other) merely one time. You must do it over and over again, with all its emotional content of tears and fear, until you are either bored with it or can actually laugh at it. Only then will you be free from its repressed emotional dynamite.

How can you reasonably expect boredom or laughter? Simple enough—after all, you are now somewhat older. You are not six. Your mother died some years ago. Isn't it silly to react at your present age as if you were still a child of six? And will all your tears erase a single moment of the past, and restore your mother to life? You are now old enough to know that the pattern of life requires death in its cycle. No one ever escapes this world alive. It is normal to fear death, and it is normal for each of us to find our own death inconceivable. But it is not normal or desirable to live in the past. The Bible says that Lot's wife looked back and turned into a pillar of salt. Don't look back; and even more important, don't live in the past as if you were still actually back there right now. When you realize that you are doing this, and that the emotionally charged patterns of past events are still bedeviling you at the subconscious level, you will understand the importance of the Guided Association method, and the need to *relive repeatedly* to the point of boredom or laughter.

How to release all stress areas of your past

You will proceed in this matter, working through the obvious emotionally charged times of your life, until you have released their internal pressures in laughter or boredom. When you have completed the obviously disturbed times of your life pattern, you will move on to the less obvious times, times of lesser stress, perhaps associated with anger, hostility, fear, and emotions not connected with tears.

When you have gone through these times, reliving them with all their emotional content, you may then experiment with the nicknames, pet names, and general distress words (Page 48). You do this by speaking these words or phrases aloud, allowing your mind to wander freely on from these general guide points to any incidents they may recall. Whatever past episodes come to mind must be relived with their full emotional content. You may be surprised to find deep, even violent, emotions connected with such times. I refer to operations, illnesses, accidents, and even to the unsuspected emotional dynamite that may be released when you start with the pet names used by your parents and relive the times that well to the surface of your thoughts when you repeat those names.

Substitute aggression—Release Therapy

It is essential to release your aggressions as fully as possible. Guided Association helps to do this in the best possible way. You release the emotionally charged, repressed memories of the past by reliving that past as if it were occurring right now. But you can go beyond this.

Another phase of Release Therapy is made possible by recognizing those whom you hate and releasing your suppressed aggression by actually pounding away at a suitable object that represents such people. The object may be a pillow pounded viciously in the privacy of your bedroom during the Guided Association session that includes such a person. Or it can take place more publicly on the golf course. If you have had an argument with your spouse, he or she is "it" when you address the golf ball. Wham, wham, wham, as you say to yourself, "That's what I think of you today. Darn you," or whatever you think is appropriate for the violence you are releasing.

But you must complete all Release Therapy sessions to the point of laughter, boredom, or forgiveness. Unless you do, be sure to go over and over such sessions, each day, until you are freed from the need for violence. This is most important.

One of my patients found a punching bag a good investment for this purpose. The actual physical device makes little difference. It is only important to let go without reserve and to get all the violence out of your system. Do this with everyone with whom you have tangled in the past and also use Release Therapy for the discharge of current desires to lash out. Do this, even if it is your own children you would like to punish, your own husband (or wife) you would like to "kill."

This is a better device than the old fashioned rolling pin, and cheaper than breaking a set of dishes. Best of all, it works quickly and easily.

Our unsuspected wellsprings of violence

Man is basically an animal. Although generally considered (by himself) to be a superior animal, this is sometimes open to question. Murder, rape, war, pillage, lynching, and killing for sport are just a few of our activities that throw some doubt on the self-evaluation of man as a superior animal. The "overkill" concept of our atomic age makes one truly wonder about the nature of man.

However, man has the potential to become a superior animal. The very fact that this potential exists makes him superior. His literature, his scientific achievements (aside from their applications to warfare), his preference for Christ, Moses, Mohammed, Buddha, Confucius, and the other religious leaders, the high respect paid the physician and the poet, all evidence man's potential to be better than he is.

But since he is basically an animal, with all the jungle's instincts still very much alive within him, let us examine these instincts and animal forms of behavior. The facts we learn about ourselves will help us to understand our own behavior patterns as well as the behavior of those we dislike, hate, or even love. These facts about our fundamental animal patterns of behavior will help us to practice Guided Association therapy and to release these wellsprings of violence as they relate to our past lives.

The animal in man

Animals live in fear. All jungle animals are constantly on the alert, wary of danger. They are ready to pounce upon an enemy if it is smaller and vulnerable—ready to flee if the enemy seems too large and powerful. Man is the same. You and I are the same.

Animals want to live. The survival instinct is strong. So is ours—normally. Animals kill for food and to protect their shelter and their young. So do we. Man is a killer by nature, but he goes animals one better. His killer instinct is generally suppressed by the laws of society, and so he kills for sport. This is an essential outlet for the sportsman, or he might very well become a killer of men. It is the reason for the popularity of violence in our television shows, the guns loved by children, the cops and robbers of their games, the prize fights of the adult, the murder and mayhem in the child's fairy tales, the murder and thirst for blood in the adult's detective stories, and his love of war. Recognize the desire, the *need* for violence within yourself, and you will be better prepared to handle your Guided Association sessions as well as your daily life.

Recognize your kinship with all other animals, and you will

begin to understand and to forgive your own tendencies to violence. Whether this violence is directed against yourself (masochism) or against others (sadism), you will see your kinship with all the violence of the world. Once you see this, you will begin to understand your dreams and desires that are full of violence, death, destruction, involving often even those you love.

Animals eat, drink, and sleep in moderation under the guidance of their basic natures. Man carries his natural needs to extremes and hastens his own death. This is a perversion of the normal animal instinct to survive. It belongs with the violence to self already described.

Animals are generally promiscuous, and marriage is a man-made institution. I am in favor of monogamy, but I am also in favor of recognizing the fact that this is not the normal condition for our basic animal nature. I would suggest that you read Kinsey if you doubt this. I would also suggest that you forgive yourself and those you love if you and they act in accordance with our deeper animal nature from time to time. Perhaps your spouse was unfaithful and you quarreled violently; work such problems out in your Guided Association session. Get rid of the tears and violence of those times, and you will be better prepared to accept the truth of your animal nature and sexual behavior.

Animals have no moral standards, no ethical rules. Man has both and generally pays no attention to them. In that respect, he remains an animal, doing what is best to assure his own survival regardless of the standards of his society. And so a hungry man steals a loaf of bread, disregards the income tax laws, or even feels that he must steal a million dollars or more.

I have known dentists who filled cavities that did not exist because they "needed" the money, and doctors who, for the same reason, performed operations to remove organs that were not diseased. And do not the major automobile manufacturers build obsolescence (both physical and psychological) into their cars just to keep us buying the new models we don't need each year? They are no more ethical than the others. But our "normal" economy depends upon the automobile manufacturer and the steel and other products he buys, so we turn away and say nothing.

Animals know neither good nor bad and act only to survive. So does man, although he pretends to know what is right and gives lip service to the Golden Rule. He attends his house of worship, planning all through the services how to make more money, how to take over another man's business, how to exploit the public. And so, despite our religions, we remain animals. Don't blame yourself for what you are. You can't help it. You must simply understand, and perhaps you will change in time. And perhaps you won't. But, if you at least understand, you will be on your way to better health, on your way to getting rid of your psychosomatic health-wreckers.

Why Guided Association works

The emotional release resulting from the repeated reliving of the grief, rage, violence, and other emotionally charged times of the past is the most crucial factor in this therapy.

It is interesting to note that a rapid decline in brain wave response to a repeated stimulus is observed in electroencephalograph experiments. This simply means that when a brain wave tracing is taken, the more the person goes over and over the disturbing factor, the less and less the brain responds. Translated into the terms of Guided Association, the more you go over and over the emotionally charged times of your life, the less they will bother your brain and body in the future. This is the basic reason for the effectiveness of this treatment, and the reason why you must relive the trouble spots repeatedly until you come to the point of laughter or boredom.

How Guided Association helps to get rid of symptoms

When treating psychosomatic illness, our goal is to find and get rid of the emotional causes of that illness. When you have gotten to the crucial point of laughter or boredom for the problem areas connected with your symptoms, your condition will be well on its way to full correction. For example, the patient with a serious disease may have had someone in his childhood, perhaps even mother or father, say, "You are no damned good. You'd be better off dead." This is accepted by the brain as a command and acts like a post-hypnotic suggestion. The patient tries to "kill" himself, and the subconscious mind acts to lower resistance or otherwise change the body functions toward a diseased state. In Guided Association, repeated reliving of this disturbing episode relieves the brain of the ancient command, and the body can now restore normal function to the "diseased" tissues.

When searching for the cause of a specific symptom, try to go back in your life to the very first time you experienced that symptom. Then relive the episode in the usual way, as if it were happening *right now*. If there does not seem to be much emotional content to this episode, relax fully, and then say to yourself, aloud:

When I count to three, the first words that will flash into my mind will be connected with my symptoms and will lead me to the time and circumstances that caused my troubles.

Work with the words revealed by your subconscious mind and you will often go directly to the earliest trouble spots, the emotional problems linked to your symptoms.

Another method, actually a way to talk to your subconscious, is to tell yourself while fully and deeply relaxed:

You will now tell me what I need to know to get better.

Your subconscious mind will usually respond with the words, time or place connected with your problem.

Another good phrase is to say, "Who tells me to have asthma (or diarrhea, constipation, or whatever your major symptom may be)?" Your subconscious mind may come up with the answer, and a picture of the person of authority in your past will flash into your mind. This will lead you to the time it occurred, and from there you need merely repeatedly relive that episode in the usual fashion, to the point of laughter or boredom.

How will you feel during Guided Association Therapy?

You will begin to improve physically and emotionally as you move from problem area to problem area, discharging the repressed emotional dynamite connected with each trouble spot of your past. There will be a spontaneous increase in energy and an increasing sense of well-being. Your symptoms will gradually disappear, even during the earliest stages of treatment. When the entire chain of emotion-charged disturbances of your past is relived and discharged, your symptoms will become a thing of the past, suitable only for discussion, laughter, or boredom, just as the emotional trouble spots themselves have become.

The truth about tranquilizers

The tranquilizing drugs cause an emotional detachment, an "I don't give a damn" feeling. This may be useful on a temporary basis, but it is hardly the goal of proper therapy in psychosomatic problems. You can get the same effect at somewhat higher cost if you drink enough alcohol. But, as with alcohol, there are side effects, and some of them are dangerous.

One type of tranquilizer causes jaundice and the shaking disease (Parkinsonism); sometimes it kills some of the white blood cells, causing a skin rash and a fever at the same time. Another type of tranquilizer also causes the shaking disease of the brain but does not cause jaundice. This type often depresses the patient, sometimes dangerously. The least toxic of these drugs is also the least effective, causing less detachment from our problems.

Since these drugs do not solve our psychosomatic disturbances and even add to them, they should be used only if all other methods of treatment fail. Naturally, they must always be taken under a physician's guidance. I have no objection to the use of the safest (and least effective) of the group, the meprobamates, but only as a temporary crutch during the type of treatment you are now learning about. For permanent help, you must get rid of the underlying emotional disturbances *without drugs*. Only the methods of relaxation therapy, Guided Association, and the others you are now learning can do this.

Practice the methods you have learned in this chapter *every day of your life*. They will lead you to better health, greater strength, a more youthful body and mind, a happier and more pleasant personality, and a longer life. They will guide you to peace of mind and will help you put an end to your psychosomatic health-wreckers. Further therapy in depth will be found in my book, UNITROL.

Points to remember:

1. You have now learned the major methods for the self-correction of your psychosomatic health-wreckers.
2. You have learned how to control your body functions.

3. You are now expert in the methods of deep relaxation and can produce such relaxation instantly.
4. You are now expert in self-suggestion methods and can stop or control pain in any part of your body.
5. You hold the major keys to personality reconstruction and peace of mind.
6. You can now change your habits of thinking, your attitudes, and feelings at will.
7. You have learned the use of the Conflict Check Chart and how to combine this with Guided Association therapy.
8. You have learned how to contact your subconscious mind to find out the disturbed life patterns of your past.
9. You have learned how to get rid of this repressed emotional dynamite in your subconscious mind.
10. Further therapy in depth will be wound in my book, UNITROL.*

---

* The UNITROL Teaching Institute, 147-41 Sanford Ave., Flushing, N.Y. 11355, will provide UNITROL information.

Chapter 6

HOW TO GET RID OF STOMACH
AND COLON PROBLEMS

How to use chapter 6

1. Check this list and see if you have any of the following symptoms:

    Abdominal (stomach) pain Regurgitation
    Poor digestion Bad breath
    Cramps Loss of appetite
    Heartburn Overeating
    Acid indigestion Bilious feelings
    Nausea Excess slime
    Vomiting in your bowel movements
    Constipation Rectal bleeding
    Diarrhea Piles
    Difficulty in swallowing Rectal pain
    A lump in your throat Rectal itch or discharge
    Sour stomach

2. If you do have any of these symptoms, read this chapter NOW.
3. Then turn back to Chapter 4 and fill out the important Conflict Check Chart.
4. Now turn to Chapter 5 and begin the simple Guided Association home sessions to get rid of your worries.
5. Now begin the Muscle Relaxation and the Self-Suggestion methods to learn how to *switch off your brain.*
6. Practice the Key Word magic for instant action in muscle relaxation, instant sleep, instant peace of mind.

In this chapter you will learn about the emotionally disturbed, upper intestinal tract and the anxious stomach and colon. As you now know, your intestinal tract, especially the large bowel, is the sounding board of the emotions. We all remember the school child (perhaps ourselves!) who fears an examination, and begins to have stomach cramps and often vomiting in the morning before leaving for school. There is absolutely nothing wrong with the youngster's intestinal tract. The nausea, cramps and vomiting are involuntary, unconscious, and serve the special purpose of organ language—telling us that the child is afraid and worried. Similarly, we have all heard of the soldier in perfect physical condition who fears going on an attack or charge. It is normal to fear death, and to face enemy gunfire and bayonets brings a strong and decisive protest from the large bowel, usually in the form of an involuntary bowel movement. These are normal, healthy, young men, usually in the very finest physical condition. There is nothing wrong with their colons. It is once again *organ language,* "speaking" of deep anxiety and fear.

You will now learn about the following interesting conditions and health-wreckers:

1. Increased salivation (wet mouth of anticipation).
2. Decreased salivation (dry mouth of fear).
3. Bad breath (odor from anxiety).
4. *Anorexia nervosa* (loss of appetite from worry).
5. *Globus hystericus* (lump in the throat).
6. Vomiting.
7. The "ball in my chest," or "I can't swallow that" feeling (cardiospasm).
8. The troubled stomach.
9. Disturbed pancreatic and bile flow.
10. Gastric-duodenal ulcer (stomach ulcer).
11. Gall bladder trouble (bile trouble).
12. The worried large bowel.

And you will learn:

1. How to eliminate constipation from your life.
2. How to prevent diarrhea.
3. The truth about mucous colitis and how to fight it (the troubled colon).

4. How ulcerative colitis (the ulcerated bowel) can be relieved.
5. The truth about hemorrhoids (piles)—prevention and
   treatment.

Increased salivation—the wet mouth

It is important to realize that we all react to words as if they
were the things represented by these words. When you and I look
at a restaurant menu, we are likely to salivate (our mouth waters)
in response to the words describing food. When we see the word
steak, we naturally think of the succulent, tasty meat itself,
cooked to our taste, rolling around in our mouth and between our
teeth, the meat juices flowing freely as we bite through the tender
morsels. This reaction is a pouring out of the normal digestive
juices in the mouth (and in the stomach). Perhaps your saliva is
flowing now, as you read this. We react to the words on the menu,
the names of foods, and the descriptive adjectives exactly as the
animals of the famous Pavlov conditioned-reflex experiment reacted to the ringing of a bell. In that experiment the noted Russian physiologist rang a bell every time food was served to his
laboratory dogs. After just a short time, he found that all he had
to do to make the digestive juices flow in the dog's mouth was to
ring the bell. The food was no longer necessary. This is called a
conditioned reflex. The animals had been trained to respond to
the sound of the bell as if it were the food itself. In the same way,
we respond to the words representing food as if they were the
food itself.

There is great variation in this response. Some of us pour out
a great deal of secretion in response to written or spoken words
and even to the very thought of food, while others react relatively
little. Generally speaking, this salivation is considered to be normal and an average reaction. Actually, it represents an emotional-
level response rather than a thinking level reaction, or a true
conditioned reflex. But it is not a disease and requires no special
treatment unless the secretion is excessive in the stomach itself.
Obviously, too much acid in the absence of food is not good for
the stomach lining.

Decreased salivation—the dry mouth

At one time or another, most of us have had the experience of a "drying up" of the mouth when we were afraid. Any painful ordeal can cause a diminished salivary secretion and even result in a total drying up of the mouth glands. In a state of extreme anxiety, fear, or pain, it is practically impossible for the average person to pour enough secretions into his mouth to allow the wetting, chewing, and swallowing of dry crackers.

Again, this is not a disease, but merely further evidence of the effect of the emotions on our body functions. No treatment is required unless you are responding in this fashion to unreasoning fear, constant anxiety, or the pressures of stress during mealtimes, preventing you from digesting and absorbing food properly. If this is your problem, you have now taken the first step toward correction by recognizing your behavior pattern. Your next step will be to work out the Conflict Check Chart (Chapter 4). You must then practice Guided Association, working from the Check Chart as described in Chapter 5. At the same time, you will be practicing the Relaxation Methods of that same chapter.

Mary Ellen R., a young housewife of 23, demonstrated an extreme case of decreased salivation. Her major complaint was not the "dry mouth," although she used this term. Her problem presented itself as nausea and a sense of fullness in the "stomach" immediately after meals. "When I begin to eat," she said, "my mouth goes dry, and I can't even wet the food enough to swallow unless I drink water or coffee with every mouthful. No matter how little I eat, my stomach begins to distend, and I feel like vomiting."

A careful examination of the intestinal tract revealed no organic disease. Exploration of the patient's emotional background, particularly by means of the Conflict Check Chart, brought out the answer. As a child she had been told by her mother that if she did not eat enough she "would dry up and her stomch would shrink." She accepted this admonition at face value and literally began to "dry up." The abdominal distention and nausea followed quite naturally, obvious organ language telling her that her stomach had indeed shrunk.

When she learned the source of her problem and the fact

that she had been interpreting her mother's words far too literally, she began to relax more at mealtime. With further training in relaxation (Chapter 5), and with the further practice of Guided Association, her symptoms rapidly disappeared.

Bad breath—your best friend won't tell you

The famous Mayo Clinic gastroenterologist, Alvarez, reports several cases illustrating the emotional cause of bad breath. He believes that drying of the mouth by "emotional stoppage of salivary secretion" may be responsible for the type of breath sometimes observed when a person is anxious or frightened, nervous or excited. He also reports that it plagues some women when they are sexually excited." Another interesting case cited by Alvarez is that of a woman "who usually has a sweet breath (but) gets a foul one whenever she is made anxious when being driven in a car along a mountain grade which for several miles skirts a precipice."

Anorexia (I'm not hungry)

This tongue twisting medical term really means a nervous loss of appetite. Mild degrees of loss of appetite during anxiety are very frequent. However, the exact opposite reaction may occur, and the overweight patient who puts on many pounds in nervous reaction to worry is well known to all of us.

The condition of extreme appetite loss is relatively rare. I have seen only one patient with this problem, a very slim young lady in her early thirties. She had been dieting intensively, not because she wanted to be attractive to men but in revulsion toward her "fat, oversexed mother." This young lady not only rebelled against food, but against anything to do with the opposite sex.

The more her mother urged her to eat, the less she would take. These problems can become very serious and may even require hospitalization and forced feeding. However, lesser degrees of refusal to eat can be managed by the various forms of therapy described in Chapter 5. It is most important that the patient be made aware of the underlying reasons for this refusal to eat. Once this awareness is brought to consciousness and worked out re-

peatedly by Guided Assocation to the point of boredom or laughter, the patient is on the way to recovery.

Psychiatrists have reported that some of these patients develop a dislike for food because they are fearful of oral impreg-
nation (the childhood idea of babies being produced from swallowing a seed). Some develop an anxiety about becoming obese
and too "sexy." And, as in the case described above, the refusal
to eat may represent a means of punishing the mother.

Globus Hystericus—I have a lump in my throat

John was a schoolboy 14 years of age. He was a very sensitive
youngster and very bright. His complaint was a "lump in my
throat." The old term *globus hystericus* means simply an emotionally produced feeling of a lump in the throat. Generally speaking, a tightness or a feeling of a lump in the throat is very
common during the state of extreme anxiety or fear or pain. Then
there are those of us who speak organ language when we say, "I
can't swallow that." Some go further and add vomiting to their
symptoms when they say, "I can't stomach that."

Although this youngster was very bright, he lived in constant fear that he would not be as "good" as his father was in
school. His father had been a Phi Beta Kappa college graduate
and was an outstanding practicing attorney. The youngster
wanted to be "as good as my Dad," and although his intelligence
was very superior, he lived in constant self-doubt.

The problem was rapidly resolved when I had both father
and son go to a psychologist for an I.Q. test on the same day.
The youngster was much relieved when he learned that his own
intelligence was actually much higher than his father's. From that
point on he became more self-reliant and lost his feeling of inferiority. The lump in the throat disappeared.

I can't stomach that

We have already described the school child who vomits in
anticipation of an examination. You have undoubtedly experienced nausea yourself, if not actual vomiting, when faced with
disturbing emotional problems. However, a careful physical examination is most important in all such cases. I remember a

famous writer and artist who had been under psychiatric treatment for three years for nausea, vomiting, and headaches before it was finally recognized that he had a brain tumor. However, although there are many possible organic causes of vomiting, in most cases the problem is functional and emotionally based.

The sour mouth

Regurgitation, the bringing up of mouthfuls of sour food without nausea, is distinguished from vomiting. Regurgitation is always functional. Then, there is the patient who forces vomiting by sticking a finger down his throat; this is usually an emotional problem. Some of us vomit with migraine headache attacks. Such attacks usually follow emotional distress, anxiety, conflict, or excitement.

Dr. Alvarez tells of the many tense, frail, oversensitive, and tired women, not pregnant, who complain of morning nausea and nausea which lasts all day: "Such nausea seems to be nervous in origin and I suspect the sensation arises from the brain and has little to do with the bowel."

I well remember a newly married young lady of 19 who did not want to have children "until we know whether or not we are going to stay together." This is a very modern viewpoint. So many marriages these days end practically during the honeymoon that it may well be a proper viewpoint for such uncertain couples. In this case the fear of pregnancy caused both nausea and vomiting. She also spoke of a constant "sour mouth." Fortunately, both she and her husband were well-instructed in contraception, and she was soon made to recognize that her fear of pregnancy was not well founded.

But there are those patients who fear pregnancy to the point where they develop a "distaste" for all sexual contact. This "distaste" may result in a sour mouth, or nausea and vomiting as a reaction to even the thought of sexual contact, and, finally, in a negative response to food. The mouth, especially the lips and tongue, is a sensitive sexual zone as well as the entry point for food. The association between a "distaste" for sex and a "distaste" for food is a natural one. In some cases these are problems requiring an extensive re-educational program for both husband and wife.

I can't swallow that

Cardiospasm, despite the sound of the word, has no direct connection with the heart or cardiac region. However, there is sometimes an indirect connection since cardiospasm refers to a functional spasm of the lower end of the tube leading from the mouth to the stomach, just at the point where this tube passes into the somach. Since the heart lies in the chest cavity just above this region, spasm of the esophagus tube may be confused with a heart attack. In some cases exactly the opposite confusion results when an actual heart attack is thought of as indigestion. Self-treatment with bicarbonate of soda may result in a fatal delay.

Functional spasm of the esophagus tube practically always represents organ language, the esophagus trying to say, "that's hard to swallow." When a problem is indeed "hard to swallow," the esophagus tightens, won't relax, and the discomfort may be very unpleasant indeed. One patient described a "tight ball in my stomach." Another said, "it is like a hand gripping my stomach." The pain may be mild or severe, and may or may not be associated with nausea. Every physician is impressed with how much the patient's state of mind influences the behavior of the esophagus. A noted practitioner reported 50 such cases, the vast majority of whom spoke of worry, aggravation, fright, or anger as the precipitating cause. This has been true in my own practice as well, and I would add anxiety, general fears, nervous excitement, and the fear of inadequacy to the list of causes. When these patients are relieved of their stress or are placed in a happier environment, the spasm and pain disappear. This can actually be proved by fluoroscope and X-ray examination.

Wherever possible, treatment requires that the patient be removed from the disturbing environment. He should be given a rest from the situation that he "cannot stand." Naturally, there are some situations that cannot be changed, and we must adjust to them. In addition to learning to adjust to environmental problems that cannot be altered, training in deep relaxation is essential. In all cases, you must find the causes of the basic, underlying conflict by careful completion of the Conflict Check Chart. The next step is Guided Association therapy to the point of boredom or laughter.

The sour stomach

Everything that I have said about our reactions to words as the actual things they represent applies most especially to stomach secretions. This is obvious when you remember your reaction to restaurant menus and even to thinking about food. It is less obvious, perhaps, but equally important to realize that when you are angered, your stomach secretions may pour out with a rush. For some of us, however, secretions actually diminish with anger, and normal stomach movements may quiet down. It may go in either direction. Usually, the reaction is an increased outpouring of gastric juices, including hydrochloric acid. If there is no food in the stomach to neutralize this acid, the danger of ulceration of the stomach lining is great. For that matter, pleasurable situations may normally increase gastric secretion, as, for example, when seated in a fine restaurant with a pleasant companion. In such cases, however, the increased secretion will be followed by food, and no harm will be done. The harm is done only if the acids are not neutralized by food.

The tone and activity of our stomach muscles are also dependent upon our attitude and emotions. Have you ever been a guest speaker at a formal dinner or a business luncheon? If you have, unless you have been conditioned by years of training, you may have had little relish for your food, and you may have suffered indigestion either before or after eating. This is a simple example of the effect of a stress situation on stomach secretion and motility. We will have more to say about this when we discuss peptic ulcer.

One of my patients experiences violent "heartburn" every time she has a quarrel with her husband, although they have been married over 20 years. This has been going on for most of that time, but she has fortunately not developed peptic ulcer. I have little doubt, however, that she will if she lives long enough. To this point, after six months of observation, she has been entirely uncooperative in all efforts to provide proper treatment. It may well be that she enjoys suffering and does not want to get well. Her suffering has brought her the sympathy and attachment of a young son, who accompanies her to every consultation and agrees with her that his father is at fault. This is basically a very unhealthy situation, and this patient cannot be made well until she recognizes the fact that she is using her illness to hold her son's affection.

Sour stomach and heartburn are very common symptoms. In most cases these symptoms are due to worry, fear, and stress, and there is no ulcer or other serious disease causing them. But, as with all psychosomatic ills, the worry increases the symptoms, and the symptoms in turn increase the worry. The final result may actually be an ulcer or worse if the vicious cycle is not broken.

Altered pancreatic and bile flow

There have been interesting experiments performed to show that when certain types of foods are suggested to a patient, a specific type of secretion occurs in both the stomach and pancreas. This latter organ produces insulin and certain digestion aids. This is a beautiful example of the relationship between words and intestinal secretion. The mere suggestion of starch and sugar foods increased the starch digesting enzymes (diastase), and no other enzymes. Oh, the power of words!

Excitement and anger can actually stop gall bladder bile flow or pancreatic digestive juices. The relationship of the emotions to the flow of digestive juices in the mouth, the stomach, the bile system, and the pancreas has been proven in experiments with both man and animals. You can accept this as a fact—your emotions will determine how well all parts of your intestinal tract function.

And so we come to the important consideration of peptic ulcer.

Peptic ulcer—its causes, palliation, and control

Peptic ulcer is a general term referring to an ulcer of either the stomach or the duodenum. The duodenum is the first part of the small intestine, immediately following the stomach. Bear in mind that the intestinal tract is a continuous tube from the mouth to the rectum. The tube through which food passes after you swallow is called the esophagus. This tube leads into the stomach, and the continuation of the intestine after the food leaves the stomach is the duodenum. The two most common locations for ulcer are the stomach lining and the lining of the duodenum.

It may well be that when the normally basic (acid-fighting) juices of the duodenum slow down and the acid juices of the stomach speed up, an ulcer develops. As you now know, such changes in secretion are often the result of emotional disturbances, stress, worry, and fear. There is no question that ulcers are usually the result of psychosomatic *worry, stress, or fear,* and there is also no question that stomach juice flow and movement are closely related to our emotions.

Many ulcer patients are well aware of their emotional problems, but many are not. Sometimes there is a suppressed hostility against the boss, a husband or wife, or some disturbing life situation, or even life in general. Some patients suffer from a feeling of defeat and submission to difficult or insurmountable problems.

I have seen cases where a child has been rejected by his parents and subsequently strives desperately for material success to build his ego. These internal pressures result in overactivity of stomach digestive enzymes and acids, and a peptic ulcer is burned into the stomach lining.

One of my patients, an important executive now in his early fifties, illustrates this perfectly. He felt that his parents were never satisfied with his behavior or his progress at school. As a result, he was always striving to do better, and developed into a neurotic perfectionist. As he carried on through life, he became over-aggressive. The result was a chronic tension state. All his activities represented a never-ending need to win approval.

In later life it was no longer the approval of his parents that he sought, but those of his associates and even of his subordinates.

A life of constant tension, the attempt to achieve a perfection that never really can be achieved, and the desire for everyone's approval (always impossible), resulted in a marked change in his stomach and small bowel behavior, and the development of a large, penetrating, duodenal ulcer. This threatened his life several times by hemorrhage and perforation.

It was only after extensive psychotherapy of the type described in this book, combined with the appropriate medical treatment, that this patient began to respond.

We must remember that all peptic ulcers are emotionally conditioned.

If you have a peptic ulcer, the diagnosis has obviously been made by your family doctor through X-ray study or some other detection method, and you are probably already on a diet and taking acid-fighting medicines. Now you must go further in order to get rid of the underlying emotional problems, both past and present.

Let's be very practical. If your job is more than you can stand, you may have to look for another. If your home life is desperate, you may have to make a change, perhaps even divorce. In other words, you must change the things you can change and adjust to those you cannot change. But don't do anything radical until you have first changed yourself. The basic FOUR-STEP METHOD of treatment will change your entire personality, your ways of looking at life, and may even relax and "toughen" you enough so that you can shrug off your boss, your home problems, and all other daily annoyances without taking it out on your own stomach and "guts."

Give yourself six months on this important crusade for better health. Practice Relaxation, Guided Association, Self-suggestion, and Substitute Aggression Release (see Chapter 5 for details) every day of your life, and you will become healthier, happier, and perhaps even younger. You will rid yourself of your psychosomatic symptoms.

Our melancholy bile

There have been some interesting medical reports showing the very close relationship of the emotions to gall bladder bile flow. It is actually possible, while under hypnosis, to give suggestions of joy, sorrow, anxiety, and annoyance to patients. Such experiments show that these suggestions cause changes in bile flow. When the patient was made to feel happy, bile flow increased almost immediately. On the other hand, annoyance almost entirely stopped the flow of bile. It is obvious that emotional disturbances can therefore cause painful spasm of the bile ducts. You would feel such pain in the upper right hand section of your abdomen, usually right underneath the rib cage on that side.

When we combine such changes in the bile system with the effects of emotional disturbance of the stomach and the small bowel, it is obvious that your digestion can be much disturbed. You might have nausea, vomiting, abdominal pain due to spasm, and even some degree of jaundice (yellow skin). Naturally, if jaundice occurs you must have a careful study for gall stones or other liver or bile duct disease.

In my own practice I have seen two cases of bile duct spasm, one with very transient jaundice, due to a combination of over-work, dissatisfaction with the nature of the work, and an un-happy home life. In both cases there was painful spasm, some heartburn, belching, nausea, and vomiting.

Both cases responded well to a combination of Guided As-sociation and Relaxation therapy. Naturally, careful attention to diet was also required.

The anxious colon

You have now learned how your emotions may cause serious disturbances in the upper part of your intestinal tract. If you are already suffering from symptoms of an anxious stomach, if there is indigestion or nervous vomiting, or spasm of the esophagus or stomach or biliary system, you know that your condition can be helped by the methods described in Chapter 5. But I must once again warn you that all such problems must be carefully studied by your family physician, and perhaps by an intestinal specialist, before you begin any self-treatment.

Now we will consider the anxious colon, teach how you can eliminate constipation from your life, how to prevent diarrhea, how to recognize and fight mucous "colitis", how to relieve ulcerative colitis, and give some facts about hemorrhoids. Every-thing you have now learned about the emotional factors respon-sible for upper intestinal disease may be applied to large bowel problems as well.

The emotionally disturbed person does not voluntarily choose the area of the intestinal tract (or other parts of the body) that will react to the emotional disturbance. We all have one or more weak links in our body structure. These overly sensi-tive, weak areas will develop symptoms first. Your organ language may come from the upper intestinal tract or the colon (large bowel) may speak to you. Your symptoms may explode in some other body region or system too. If you develop a worried bowel, you may show evidence of overactivity (diarrhea) and excess mucus (slime) secretion, or underactivity with constipation and dry stools, or actual inflammatory disease with ulcerations and bleeding. And believe it or not, even hemorrhoids (piles), fissures, an ulcer, fistulae, and other lower bowel diseases may be emotionally based. In my *Handbook of Psychosomatic Medicine*, written for the physician, I have pointed out that cancer of the bowel may have its beginnings in emotional disturbances. I do not wish to overly emphasize this point, but if you will realize that emotional disturbances can readily produce bowel ulcerations and that this ulcerative colitis is complicated by cancer in a fairly large number of cases, you will see the probable causative sequence of events. This is not to say that those of us who are bedevilled by emotional problems will ultimately develop cancer. Not at all. But it does mean that we may be laying the groundwork for some serious intestinal changes, allowing chronic irritation (or perhaps a virus) to ultimately cause cancer.

Mucous colitis and how to fight it

Mucous colitis is not really a colitis. There is no inflammation of the colon (the *-itis* ending usually means inflammation, like appendic*itis*). The term colitis is, therefore, a misnomer. The better term for this condition is "irritable colon."

This is a condition that usually occurs in individuals with an unstable central or autonomic nervous system (Chapter 14 describes this nervous system in simple language). Irritable colon may occur together with irritable heart (See the next chapter on "How to Surmount Your Heart and Blood Vessel Problems").

If you are experiencing symptoms of the irritable colon (the worried bowel), you may have some degree of abdominal discomfort, either diarrhea or constipation. If you have diarrhea, it is because your irritable bowel is overactive. If you are constipated, it may be because your irritable colon is spastic, the tightness of the muscle holding back the stool contents of the bowel. Or, there may be associated spasm of the muscles at the outlet of the rectum, and perhaps even some local inflammation at the outlet of the rectum. It is unusual to find large bowel disease without associated rectal disease. Be certain that your physician always checks both large bowel and rectum, not only with X-ray but also by passing a lighted tube into the rectum and sigmoid, so that he can look at the lining directly. This tube is called a *sigmoidoscope* and the examination is known as a *sigmoidoscopy*.

It is safe to say that if sigmoidoscopy were performed as a routine part of every physical examination, those conditions that ultimately result in cancer of the rectum would be observed and removed. This is one of the most fertile areas for preventive medicine, especially for the prevention of cancer.

What does this have to do with you? You will be interested to know that in one study of 40,000 off-the-street men and women, people with no symptoms relating to the large bowel, examined in a cancer detection center, eight per cent had pre-cancerous conditions or actual cancer. Translated into other terms, this means that of the next 100 people you meet, people with no symptoms relating to the large bowel or the rectum, eight of them may be candidates for cancer of the lower bowel. These are frightening figures, and demonstrate the tremendous importance of a careful lower bowel examination as a routine part of every semiannual physical examination. If your physician does not do such studies, please ask for referral to a proctologist (a rectal specialist).

You will be interested to know that in my own practice there are many more females than males who suffer from an irritable bowel. Some physicians report the ratio of female to male as five to one. Every one of these cases is associated with some degree of nervous or mental strain (psychosomatic), and the majority are young or middle-aged adults.

One of my most interesting cases was a fireman who was moonlighting as a taxi driver. Curiously enough, he was most relaxed and felt best while driving a cab but lived in constant fear for his life while in the fire house. This resulted in excess colon activity, the passage of large amounts of mucous with his stool, and frequent, loose bowel movements. He passed occasional blood as well, but this was found to be due to hemorrhoids (varicose veins in the rectum) that were being irritated by the frequent bowel movements.

He responded beautifully to the FOUR-STEP METHOD of treatment, and became very expert at Instant Relaxation. As he relaxed and combined this with Self-suggestion of the very general type ("every day, in every way, my bowels are becoming better and better"), his movements became more formed and less frequent.

The Conflict Check Chart showed no serious problems in his past, but emphasized the violent reaction he was having to his job in the fire department. He had a very natural fear of death, just like all the rest of us. Daily Guided Association sessions in his own home helped him "let off steam" on this fear. He relived the time when one of his "buddies" was killed during a fire; and when he had done this over and over again, he finally found that he could face the memory of the past without it "getting to my guts."

Fortunately, he was near the retirement stage, and his problem was solved upon retiring. He then became a full time taxi driver and has had practically no symptoms since. Of course, I removed his hemorrhoids in the usual painless, ambulatory (you walk out and drive home!) fashion in my office, and he was back at work the next day.

Since most cases occur in women, let me tell you about Mrs. R. L., a 31-year-old housewife. Although she had been married for only two years, she and her husband lived in a constant state of bickering, the quarrels usually due to insufficient funds. They were living well above their economic heads, driving large cars, and associating with the mink coat set.

In this case, there were alternating bouts of constipation and diarrhea, and the passage of tremendous amounts of mucous with each stool. Each evening she went to bed with a distended abdomen and cramps. This further complicated the matter by reducing marital sex. The problem was made still worse by the husband's rather crude threat to, "take my business elsewhere."

When she realized what she was doing, after several stormy Guided Association sessions, she began to laugh at herself. "I have been stupid," she concluded bitterly.

This realization helped reduce the frequency of the evening "loose bowels," but they were not completely controlled until there had been a drastic change in spending habits. The combination of appropriate anti-spasm medicines, training in relaxation and Guided Association, and the changed economic situation resulting from these forms of guidance, ultimately corrected her condition. A happy family life resulted, and a much healthier and younger patient.

How ulcerative colitis can be relieved

We don't know the cause of the ulcerated bowel. There seems to be a general agreement, however, that emotional disturbances are the root of many, and perhaps most, cases. It may be that some bacteria or virus will ultimately be found to be responsible, either directly or indirectly. In all probability we will learn that the emotions are the major element, and bacterial invasion is superimposed upon the colon changes resulting from emotional disturbances.

I have even seen one case of mucous colitis that became ulcerative. A 20-year-old truck driver had suffered from "colitis" for three years before consulting me. The colitis began shortly after a head-on collision while driving his truck. The steering wheel had struck his abdomen just underneath the breast bone. His brother-in-law, whom he disliked, was riding as a passenger and was entirely uninjured.

Two days later this young man consulted his local physician with a conviction that he had cancer of the stomach. X-ray studies showed no disease of the stomach or of the colon. He then "transferred" his symptoms to the colon, with resulting diarrhea. The family physician diagnosed "colitis."

He was referred for study, and examination of the large bowel showed no ulcerations, and no other organic disease of the bowel. However, while under observation and study, he began to develop a gradual transition from a typical irritable colon of mucous colitis to the ulceration and bleeding of classical ulcerative colitis.

Treatment required extensive psychotherapy, Guided Association and a reliving of the accident as well as of the patient's unhappy contacts with his brother-in-law, and training in relaxation therapy. These are the methods you have already learned. Of course, this was associated with careful local treatment to the involved colon. The combination helped greatly, especially when the patient was finally convinced that he had no "cancer." After three months of treatment his symptoms disappeared and the ulcerations cleared. Fourteen years later—he had had no recurrence and is living a happier life.

Most cases of ulcerative colitis are due to chronic emotional tension, the emotions acting through the autonomic nervous system to produce changes in colon function and ultimate ulcerations and bleeding. But you must remember that the ulcerations are a result of more than emotional factors. Increased muscle activity in the large bowel, increased secretions, the passage of large amounts of upper small intestinal digestive secretions into the colon, secondary bacterial invasion, spasm of blood vessels, and nutritional deficiency may all be factors in the production of the actual ulcerations. Recognizing this, you will realize that your physician must correct all of these conditions at the same time that he helps you in the control of your emotional disturbances.

What type of emotional problems can cause ulcerative colitis? The answer runs the gamut of the entire Conflict Check Chart.

Most ulcerative colitis patients are of average or high intellectual ability. Many are perfectionists; the housewives are usually "neat and fussy." Marital incompatibility or poor adjustment in sex life is observed in practically all cases. In many, there are financial troubles. Young men may have an abnormal emotional attachment to their mother.

I remember a 52-year-old widow who developed ulcerative colitis over a ten-year period during the last ten years of her husband's life. Her married life had been very distasteful, and she hated her husband. This hatred was generalized to include all men.

And so, she discouraged all men who showed the least interest in her 22-year-old daughter. The daughter finally became her mother's constant companion and nurse. The demanding mother required so much of her attention that her boy friends were rapidly discouraged. In this case the colitis was obviously a mechanism employed by the mother to enslave her daughter.

I advised both mother and daughter that they must have treatment and guidance together if we were to help the ulcerative colitis. The mother received the usual treatment for ulcerative colitis, together with the various forms of psychotherapy described in Chapter 5. The daughter was made to recognize the abnormal relationship between herself and her mother and was gently informed that her mother would not get well until she had lived through the "crisis" of seeing her daughter married. The daughter soon obtained work, arranged for her own apartment away from home, and the ultimate result was marriage. For a time her mother became worse, and the daughter developed an enormous sense of guilt. However, with proper guidance her mother gradually improved, and the final result for both was a happy one.

Another interesting case was that of a 40-year-old physician who had recurring episodes of ulcerative colitis over a 20-year period. His attacks were becoming increasingly severe, and characterized by acute episodes of diarrhea and the passage of large amounts of bright red blood.

The doctor enjoyed playing golf but had to take a roll of toilet paper with him every time he played. In all stress situations, whether golf or bridge, his diarrhea increased, and he developed a fever as high as 101° and up. At other times, the diarrhea was less frequent and he had no fever.

His pre-medical and medical education were financed by an older brother. Shortly after his graduation from medical college, the older brother lost his business, and he himself required assistance. However, the patient was unable to help his brother inasmuch as his colitis developed shortly after entering practice. This reduced his activity in practice and his earnings. It was evident that the colitis provided an escape from the obligation to repay his debts. The doctor was fearful of his abilities to succeed in practice and did not realize that the early years are always relatively inadequate financially. To justify his expected failure, he developed colitis; the colitis providing a perfectly "logical reason for failing."

Although physicians are notoriously poor patients, in this case the response to combined training in relaxation and his Guided Association sessions was very good indeed. Within six months, the bleeding was fully controlled, the diarrhea had stopped, and he could even play golf or bridge without the accompanying roll of toilet paper. He was also able to spend a good deal more time in his practice, and he proved to be a very successful and competent physician.

Many of these colitis patients are convinced that they have cancer simply because of bloody bowel movements. I remember one 62-year-old woman who had very active rectal bleeding. She was referred by her family physician for the removal of obviously large, bleeding hemorrhoids. However, she herself was convinced that she had cancer.

She had lost 22 pounds in weight during the 6 months before her visit to my office. Careful examination, by both sigmoidoscope and by X-ray, showed no evidence of cancer. She was carefully reassured, and the hemorrhoids were removed in the usual painless, office method. She came back to the office the next day for a dressing, free from pain, and much happier. She soon regained her weight. However, the next cancer education campaign that hit the newspapers resulted in a recurrence of her symptoms and loss of weight. Again, reassurance after examination was effective, and she regained the lost weight.

The next time I saw her, she had active ulcerative colitis involving the rectum and the adjacent large bowel to a high level. She had been reading a book on cancer and was convinced that her cancer had been overlooked by all physicians, including myself. Careful study was performed, and this time extensive psychotherapy followed. She was trained to relax during all her working hours. She was also given a number of books on cancer so that she could read them during her treatment, and have all her questions answered. Since it is impossible to avoid exposure to the recurrent cancer campaigns and the continuing material on cancer that finds its way into the women's magazines and the newspapers, it was thought best to inoculate her with a large dose of literature. This treatment proved to be quite effective, and she has had no recurrence of her anxiety, cancer phobia, or her colitis during the past six years.

A word of caution is in order. It is important for you to understand that the emotional factor is only one of many possible causes of ulcerative colitis. You must also understand that the disease itself causes severe changes in general and local bowel function, requiring treatment even after the emotional conflicts are resolved. Even though there may be a strong emotional background in any case, careful attention to diet is required after the bleeding is brought under control. In some cases a change in environment is essential. Whether this will be in terms of frequent vacations or a change of job, a new town, or even a new wife or husband, can only be determined after careful study in each individual case. Careful guidance after the Conflict Check

Chart has been fully explored, careful Guided Association therapy, and careful training in relaxation methods will all be important elements in the battle against ulcerative colitis. But in every case, the patient must realize that he will eventually need to fight his own battles if the improvement is to be sustained.

How to eliminate constipation from your life

In 1962 I wrote a book called *Control of Constipation*. In this book I pointed out that one of the most essential body functions is too often made the subject of crude and vulgar joking. This attitude has literally caused many deaths because of the feelings of shame that result in putting off treatment of serious bowel disorders until it is too late. A change in bowel habit, particularly constipation, may be evidence of some serious disease. Constipation may even be evidence of cancer of the large bowel.

However, most chronic constipation sufferers have functional, emotion-based problems. On the other hand, there are a number of specific diseases which may cause constipation. These include thyroid deficiency (the lazy thyroid) and diabetes. Both of these are easily discovered by your physician by simple blood tests. Another disease that can cause constipation is excessive activity of the parathyroid glands (located near the thyroid). In some cases constipation may be due to an actual organic obstruction in the intestinal tract. Diverticulitis (an inflammation of protruding pouches in the large bowel) is a common cause of constipation. Interestingly enough, colon pouches are found in practically everyone over 40 years of age. Liver and gall bladder diseases are also a cause of constipation. Hemorrhoids, both internal and external, are commonly associated with constipation, either as cause or effect. Internal hemorrhoids (inside piles) may actually cause a partial obstruction to the passage of a shaped stool. Since there may be no pain associated with simple hemorrhoids during a bowel movement, and since passed blood may be easily overlooked, regular examinations are necessary to detect these varicose veins (hemorrhoids) while they are still easily corrected in the office.

Spasm of the sphincter muscle at the outlet of the rectum may cause a temporary or even a chronic constipation. This spasm may result from inflammation of the rectal outlet or from internal and external hemorrhoids.

Weakness of the colon muscles, poor diet, or tumors may also be factors in the cause of constipation. Obviously, you must see your doctor at once if you are suffering from chronic constipation.

And if your physican does not do a careful examination of the large bowel, including looking into the bowel through a lighted signmoidoscope tube, please ask for referral to a specialist. It is much too important to take chances with constipation.

Your colon, your conflicts, and constipation

Once organic disease has been ruled out, you and your physician must do a careful study of the emotional factors in your constipation. Your physician must satisfy himself that your involuntary nervous system (the autonomic nervous system) is in good balance. Otherwise, the sounding board of the emotions, the colon, will be played upon with great violence during even the slightest emotional storm.

During periods of emotional stress, most of us lose control of our reactions, and the autonomic nervous system goes berserk. This causes exaggerated reactions throughout the intestinal tract and, most especially, in the colon. If the same emotional storms are repeated often enough or are continuous, the large bowel may suffer severe organic damage as you already know. Certainly, constipation is a frequent result.

Since our psychosomatic problems may have their origins in early childhood as well as during adult life, it is most important that you carefully complete your Conflict Check Chart. The next step, of course, is Guided Association therapy and, of equal importance, very careful training in relaxation. When you have learned to relax the voluntary muscles of your body, you will then be in a better position to relax your generally involuntary large bowel muscles.

I remember well the problem of constipation presented by a 38-year-old man who suffered from rectal bleeding. Examination showed both internal and external hemorrhoids caused by chronic constipation. Further studies showed all the symptoms of an unstable autonomic nervous system. He sweated excessively although the examining room was air conditioned. He told me that the palms of his hands were continuously "sweaty," and his hands trembled slightly. His reflexes were overactive. He suffered from excessive flushing of various parts of the body, most especially his neck and face. His hands and feet were cold, and his pulse rate showed a considerable variation, being rapid most of the time.

This patient did not eat properly, practically no fruits or vegetables. This poor diet did not provide sufficient roughage for his colon. The Conflict Check Chart showed that he identified himself with his father, who had died of cancer of the colon 12 years earlier. He had remembered that his father's cancer had caused severe constipation and, finally, intestinal obstruction. His own constipation had convinced him that he also had developed a cancer. Naturally, he blamed the constipation on this imaginary malignancy.

Our very careful examination ruled out the possibility of organic disease, and I finally convinced the patient that he did not have a cancer. Nevertheless, this conviction was on a thinking level, and the feeling level continued to refuse to believe. The constipation remained.

Extensive self-treatment of the type found in Chapter 5, especially the reliving of experiences through Guided Association, eliminated his identification with his father and his unconscious belief that all constipation must be caused by cancer. This treatment was combined with proper diet and the re-establishment of a regular bowel habits. It was also necessary to remove his hemorrhoids, a simple procedure that is done in the office with painless, bloodless ambulatory methods.

Again, a word of caution. Treatment of psychosomatic constipation may require long periods of Guided Association and relaxation training. During this time it is essential to correct the laxative habit by staying away from all laxatives. You must eat properly and develop regularity in exercise, sleep, and bowel movement timing. Regular warm baths may be very helpful during your training in relaxation. And the final important note of caution—see your physician before beginning any treatment. Don't be afraid to go. Proper examination is quite painless, and even the correction of rectal conditions such as hemorrhoids, fistulas, anal ulcer, cryptitis, or fissures, is easily managed in the well-equipped office, without pain, without hospitalization, and with little loss of time from work.

The truth about hemorrhoids

Hemorrhoids are varicose veins in the rectum. You have all seen varicose veins in the legs, due to gravity and weak vein walls. Similar weakening of the vein walls may occur in the rectum, again due partly to gravity, but also to straining at stool, constipation, diarrhea, and many other local factors. Practically everyone develops hemorrhoids before they have gotten out of their teens. Pregnancy becomes a major causative factor a little later in life. In such cases, the constipation produced by the actual obstruction of the rectum as the womb enlarges and presses backward, is the major cause of the hemorrhoids.

Hemorrhoids are commonly called "piles," and may develop inside or outside the rectum. If both internal and external hemorrhoids are present at the same time, the condition is called mixed hemorrhoids.

External hemorrhoids, which are covered by the skin around the anus, should not be confused with internal hemorrhoids which have prolapsed (fallen out of the rectum). The treatment for each type of hemorrhoids is entirely different.

It is safe to say that practically every adult has hemorrhoids. In fact, some varicose veins in the rectum are occasionally found in children, and have been reported in newborn infants. They are found equally in both sexes.

Another important factor in the cause of hemorrhoids is probably the poor diet of civilized man, constipation resulting. The laxative habit also plays an important role. And then, there is the refusal of many people to respond to the urge to have a bowel movement, an urge that may come while they are busy entertaining or at work. This not only makes the constipation worse, but also increases the pressure on the hemorrhoidal veins. If straining becomes necessary to pass a stool, the rectal veins bulge and weaken.

Since constipation and diarrhea are major causes of hemorrhoids, and since both are often due to emotional problems, it is obvious that hemorrhoids often indirectly result from such emotional disturbances.

Internal hemorrhoids may become very large without causing any symptoms at all. Bleeding, however, is the most obvious symptom. In fact, internal hemorrhoidal veins may rupture and cause severe hemorrhage. Or, either internal or external hemorrhoids may clot, a condition called "thrombosed hemorrhoids." The veins then become very tender, and there is sudden sharp pain while sitting, and even while walking. If the clotted vein ruptures, severe bleeding may occur.

In later stages, internal hemorrhoids may protrude. Sometimes the entire rectal wall weakens, and the lining membrane falls outside the opening. Or the internal hemorrhoids become inflamed and chronically irritated, the resulting mucus discharge irritating the skin around the anus and causing "itching piles."

While most people who suffer from hemorrhoids do not develop cancer, there have been some reports of cancer in hemorrhoidal tissue. That is why it is best to play it safe and remove hemorrhoids.

The removal of hemorrhoids can be a simple, painless, practically bloodless, office procedure. Long-lasting anesthetics are available to keep the surgical area practically free from pain for as long as a month. During this time the wounds heal, making the entire procedure, even during the healing stage, relatively free from discomfort. Our patients usually drive their own car home after removal of hemorrhoids in the office, and are back at work within a day or two at the most.*

In all such cases it is important to correct the underlying causes. Constipation and diarrhea must be brought under control, using the various methods described above. Training in relaxation is especially important in bringing a spastic bowel and rectal outlet under control.

The Four-Step Method

The basic treatment for all psychosomatic problems is the FOUR-STEP METHOD, as demonstrated in Chapter 4, p. 50. These

---

* Described in the author's book, *Painless Office Rectal Treatment* (available from the UNITROL Teaching Institute, 147-41 Sanford Ave., Flushing, N.Y.).

are the four steps you follow after checking with your doctor to see if your problems are organic or psychosomatic in nature:

1. You outline your life story and family history of disease and causes of death. You stress your fears, especially your health and death fears.

2. You fill out your Conflict Check Chart, locating times of worry, stress, injury, tears, grief, violence, and all other emotional disturbances from birth to the present moment.

3. You see your physician for examination, explanation, and reassurance. Follow his advice.

4. You then rid yourself of these worries and fears—both past and present—by practicing the methods of Chapter 5:

> Self-Suggestion and Instant Relaxation
> Guided Association
> Substitute Aggression Release

The symptoms of your psychosomatic health-wreckers are brought under control by these simple, do-it-yourself methods.

This basic FOUR-STEP METHOD is the one used by every one of the patients you will read about in this chapter and in every succeeding chapter of this book. It is the method you must use.

The following case history illustrates the basic FOUR-STEP METHOD in the treatment of the average stomach and colon problem:

Alice was the average housewife, troubled by mounting food costs, clothing costs for herself and her two youngsters, and the limited income of her hard-working husband. John supplemented his income by holding down two jobs, but there never seemed to really be enough. The installment payments, the mortgage payments, and the everyday costs of living kept them running as fast as they could just to stand still.

Alice began to complain of headache, backache, a sour stomach with acid coming up into her mouth after every meal, and a general feeling of being "run down."

My examination showed no organ changes, no serious disease, but Alice was sick. She had very real psychosomatic stomach symptoms, and they were making her life miserable. I explained this to her and reassured her that there were no ulcers, no cancer, and no other serious diseases. (This would have been Step 3 of the FOUR-STEP METHOD if you were following the routine as outlined for the average reader).

I then asked her to fill out the Conflict Check Chart (Step 2), since I had already taken her personal and family history (Step 1) at the time of her initial examination. She did this and found several areas of emotional trouble in her past and in her family history. Her mother had died when Alice was only 12, and she thought it was from a "stomach hemorrhage." This had been a time of grief for Alice, and she relived this episode with much crying during her Guided Association sessions. She did this at home, and reported that she felt much better after she had carried on to the point of boredom. "There were no more tears," as she put it; and when there were no more tears, there was no more subconscious worry about this sad time in her early life.

This is a major element of the Guided Association treatment, as you now know. You must relive the times of grief, pain, and stress, over and over again, until you are bored or amused. At that point, you realize that you have been living too much in the past, making a mountain out of a molehill, or living and thinking and worrying today as if you were still the child of yesterday. It is then that you literally "grow up." It is at that point that your psychosomatic symptoms begin to vanish.

By practicing Guided Association each day in the privacy of her own bedroom, Alice worked her way through each of the worry spots of the past. At the same time, she was becoming expert in Self-Suggestion and Relaxation Control. She looked better, felt better, and saw the change in herself with each passing day. She had mastered instant sleep, and she now could relax whenever she wished. This was a "great blessing," and she realized that her headaches were disappearing as she became more and more expert in full-time muscle relaxation.

She also used Substitute Aggression Release, directing her anger against her husband and pounding her pillow to let off this repressed steam. "I feel great, after I do this," she confessed. "After all, it's not his fault that he doesn't make 50,000 dollars a year. He works hard and is a good provider, and I love him." She realized that letting off steam in this way was better than holding it in and taking it out on herself in terms of headache, acid indigestion, and other symptoms.

Points to remember:

1. The intestinal tract, especially the large bowel, is the sounding board of the emotions.
2. The organ language of the intestinal tract includes:
   a. the dry mouth of fear
   b. the wet mouth of anticipation
   c. the bad breath of anxiety
   d. the anxious loss of appetite
   e. the "I don't care" of nervous overeating
   f. the "ball in the throat" of "I can't swallow that"
   g. the vomiting of "I can't stomach that"
   h. the peptic ulcer of despair and fear
   i. the anxious colon
   j. the constipation of rejection
   k. the diarrhea of rebellion, worry or fear
   l. the mucous colitis that isn't a colitis
   m. the ulcerative colitis of emotional imbalance
3. You must remember always to see your physician first, before beginning the self-treatment of the emotional factors.
4. Even if your condition is partially organic, there is always an emotional component.
5. You must learn to fight your own battles, and you now have the help of the Conflict Check Chart, Guided Association, the Instant Relaxation methods, and Substitute Aggression Release (THE FOUR-STEP METHOD).

Chapter 7

HOW TO SURMOUNT HEART
AND BLOOD VESSEL PROBLEMS

How to use chapter 7

1. Check this list and see if you have any of the following symptoms:

   Chest or heart pain or discomfort
   Pain with exertion or after eating—in your chest, under your
      breast-bone, or down your left arm
   Palpitation
   Difficult breathing
   Swollen ankles
   Fear of heart disease
   Anxiety after being told of a heart murmur
   Worry after being told of high blood pressure
   Chest pressure
   Worry after a friend or relative died of a heart attack
   Rapid heart
   Awareness of heart beat
   Pounding in chest or ears
   Shortness of breath
   Fatigue and heart worry generally

2. If you do have any of these symptoms, read this chapter now.
3. Then, turn back to Chapter 4 and fill out the basic Conflict
   Check Chart.
4. Now, turn to Chapter 5 and begin the simple Guided Association home sessions to get rid of your worries.

5. Now, begin the Muscle Relaxation and the Self-Suggestion Methods to learn how to Switch Off Your Brain.
6. Practice the KEY WORD magic for instant action in muscle relaxation, instant sleep, instant peace of mind, etc.

How to soothe the anxious heart

In this chapter you will learn about today's number one killer, heart disease. You will learn the causes of heart and vital blood vessel disease and how to avoid them.

You will be amazed by the simple Longevity Diet, a gourmet diet you can enjoy all your life. And you will be even more astonished to find that this diet will not only prolong your life, but will give you a new, svelte figure—without even trying. If you are overweight, fat will melt away and redistribution will take place, leaving your body softly rounded and firm, rather than flabby. The burden on your heart pump will be gone forever.

You will also learn the other key causes of sudden heart death, and how to avoid them. There are nine roads to heart disaster, and eight of them can be rerouted to safety. You will be given the road map for heart health, clearly marked and posted.

You will also learn that not all chest pain is heart pain. This is important reassurance, and will save you much unnecessary anxiety and suffering. It may rescue you from becoming a self-induced, cardiac cripple.

You will learn about the anxious heart, the irritable heart, and the happy heart. You will learn how and when to exercise to help prevent heart disease.

But best of all, this chapter teaches you how to prevent and control heart and blood vessel disease in a way that will lengthen your life, increase your general vitality, and strengthen other vital body organs at the same time. You will learn how others have done it, and you will start at once on the simple methods to prolong your own life.

The number one killer

Heart disease is now the number one cause of death in the United States. For that matter, it is the number one cause of death in every civilized country.

A diet containing a high proportion of saturated animal fats, excessive carbohydrates and starches, and too many calories is the major killer factor. The vulnerable coronary arteries that supply blood to the never-sleeping heart muscle may be clogged with deposits of cholesterol, on which the fatal clot forms. (See Chapter 8, p. 139 for details of the gourmet, life-saving diet).

But there is more to heart and blood vessel disease than diet. There are the factors of stress, your emotions, deficient exercise, neuro-psychic elements, tobacco, anxiety, a resistance to relaxation, and, finally, your individual, genetic structure.

The sedentary disease

If we consider coronary disease as a SEDENTARY disease, we can find the key causative elements in the word itself:

S	Stress
E	Emotions
D	Diet
E	Exercise (deficiency or competitive)
N	Neuro-psychic
T	Tobacco
A	Anxiety
R	Relaxation resistance
Y	You (your genetic structure)

The exact role of stress in coronary disease is not yet fully known. It would appear that it acts in several ways at least:

1. When you are in distress, the cholesterol level in your blood tends to rise.
2. Under stress, your adrenal glands pour adrenaline into your blood stream, and this raises your blood pressure and increases your heart rate.
3. Many of your blood vessels tend to contract during stress, decreasing the blood flow to the tissues supplied by these vessels.
4. Chemical changes take place in the constitution of your blood stream and your tissues during stress. This has been carefully studied and reported by Dr. Hans Selye, the famed Montreal stress researcher. Stress causes changes in the mineral constituents of the blood stream that predispose the body to death of heart muscle.

Not all pain is heart pain

Are there other ways in which stress, emotions, anxiety influence the heart? There are many ways. First, a word of reassurance. Most patients who have symptoms in the heart region (the left chest) have no organic heart disease. Aside from anxiety, pain in the left side of the chest may be due to disorders of nerves, neuritis; muscular problems; inflammation of the lining of the chest cavity (pleurisy); inflammation within the lung itself; disorders of the diaphragm (the muscular partition separating the chest from the abdominal cavity below); disturbances in the esophageus and stomach; or even excessive gas in the stomach pressing against the diaphragm on the left. There are other organic causes of pain in the left chest, and you must always consult your physician before leaping to an unwarranted self-diagnosis of heart disease.

It is natural to think of the heart first whenever you have symptoms in the heart region. After all, most of us are aware of the very high frequency of heart disease. We know of friends, neighbors, or even relatives who have died of heart failure or coronary closure. And isn't the heart the symbolic seat of the emotions? Because of this one factor alone, whether your left chest pain is due to stress or organic disease elsewhere in the body, you immediately focus your attention on the heart.

Organ language

So much of our body language is centered on the heart. Think of the expressions, "broken-hearted," "faint-hearted," "heavy-hearted," "chicken-hearted," "hard-hearted," "warm-hearted," "heartless," "heartfelt," "light-hearted," "heartache," "heart-sick," —all directing our attention to this fundamental organ, this focal point of anxiety and stress.

Even the physician may inadvertently direct the patient's emotions and attention to his heart. A slight murmur is very common after 40 years of age. The physician who mentions this heart murmur during the course of his examination may be planting seeds of chronic cardiac anxiety. Naturally, this is a misinterpretation on the part of the patient, and unintentional on the part of the physician. Nevertheless, medicine has a name for such disease, resulting from this misinterpretation in the physician-patient relationship—*iatrogenic disease.*

Physician-caused anxiety

The physician need merely look concerned, or raise his eyebrows in a questioning fashion while placing his stethoscope over the chest. This may be enough for the sensitive and overanxious patient. He reacts to the expressions on the physician's face, the emotionally charged atmosphere of the examining room, his own internal anxieties, his fears—in brief, to all words and symbols of the past and present. The result is an acute and, perhaps later, chronic, cardiac neurosis.

Such anxiety and neurosis produce tremendous physiological changes. As you already know, these changes may damage the cardiovascular system. Indeed, the heart is the most vulnerable organ in the body in its response to any anxiety state. Since time immemorial, physicians have been aware of this fact. Physiologists have described evidences of the central position of the heart and blood vessels in the emotional-reaction structure of all human beings (and, indeed, of other animals as well).

The anxious heart defined

What do we mean by *cardiac neurosis?* This term is properly used for functional heart disturbances resulting from anxiety and stress. But we must also remember the fact that anxiety may aggravate organic heart disease and even precipitate a *severe* heart attack. Then, of course, we are no longer dealing with a cardiac neurosis, but more truly with an organically based condition aggravated by stress and anxiety. Under any circumstances, whether we are dealing with a normal heart that is not functioning properly because of worry, or a diseased heart that is further disturbed by anxiety, the key element is the *anxiety.* For the moment, let us consider only the relationship of anxiety to the normal heart—true cardiac neurosis. What are the precipitating causes of the anxious heart?

A careful study of patients with cardiac neurosis shows that many of them had "nervous breakdowns" at one time or another, either during their early life or later, always resulting from stress. We have already mentioned the unintentional iatrogenic reaction when the patient misinterprets the physician's expressions or statements. This occurs often these days when young men are examined for Army service. It has been noted frequently during the course of insurance examinations as well, particularly if a large policy is being issued and several physicians are called in for consultation—among them heart specialists. Although this is routine when large policies are issued, as are electrocardiograms, the patient may misinterpret this as an indication of heart disease.

If you have ever reacted in this fashion during or after an examination by your physician, and if you are still fearful of heart disease, you need further reassurance. This reassurance must come from a careful examination by a competent heart specialist. But even more than that, you need careful study and understanding of the basic emotional, psychological, and environmental problems that are the real roots of your underlying anxiety. This underlying anxiety is merely expressing itself as a cardiac neurosis. It could just as well have been a cancer neurosis or some other form of organ-language disorder.

Another important, precipitating factor producing the anxious heart condition is an early, disturbing stress or anxiety episode. Such an anxiety state usually causes a rapid heart action and awareness of this heart action by the patient (palpitation). This, in turn, may lead the physician to suspect heart disease. The final link in the chain is the patient's own interpretation or misinterpretation of the physician's diagnosis, and the ultimate cardiac neurosis results.

As we have already mentioned, when a friend or relative dies of a heart attack, it is natural for you to become concerned about your own heart. Even reading the newspaper obituary page and noting cardiac deaths in our own age group may be enough to precipitate an anxiety state. The ultimate result may be cardiac neurosis—the anxious heart.

R.J.'s story illustrates some of these factors: R.J., 27-year old executive, had many financial problems. Although he owned his own home, it was heavily mortgaged, and the mortgage payments were difficult for him to manage. The same could be said for his Cadillac convertible, his boat, and even his country club membership. He considered all of these essential to his executive position, his social and business needs. He had no children, but his wife made up for this by her demanding immaturity. Further, he was not "sure of her," and suffered the continuous anxiety of jealousy.

When he first consulted a physician for an insurance examination, he mentioned "occasional palpitation," and this resulted in consultation with a cardiologist at the home office of the insurance company. Nothing organic was found, and he was passed for insurance at normal rates. However, the very fact that a cardiologist had been called in consultation convinced this young man that he had a heart condition. Soon after, he began to complain of increasing palpitation after a round of golf, some shortness of breath, and an occasional twinge of pain "in my heart." To complicate matters, he began to develop diarrhea and the passage of a large amount of mucous with each stool.

Careful examination of this patient's cardiovascular status and intestinal tract revealed no evidence of organic disease. It was a typical hyperactive colon resulting from anxiety (sometimes incorrectly called "mucous colitis"). The palpitation, shortness of breath, and pain in the left chest were all the results of the basic anxiety which centered on the heart in consequence of the patient's misinterpretation of the insurance examination and his "heartache" over his wife.

Careful explanation of these factors was given to the patient. He required the understanding that arose from the completion of the Conflict Check Chart and the release of emotional tensions about his wife's fidelity.

The basic financial problem had not been resolved, and will probably continue to be a source of anxiety to this man no matter how high he moves on the executive scale or how much he earns. This is a common problem of the organization man in today's highly competitive business life.

The happy heart

The major importance of stress and emotional disturbance in heart attack seems demonstrated by a recent report from Roseto, Pennsylvania. This little town is only 110 miles from New York City and is composed of people of Italian descent who love prosciutto ham with an inch of fat on it, fried peppers, and bread dipped in lard gravy, with plenty of Chianti to wash it all down.

Not only that, they are fat, hard-working, and happy people. It is said that they are "without a care for tomorrow." In spite of this diet, these happy people of Italian descent do not often die of heart attacks.

A report in one of the leading medical journals on the town of Roseto showed that they had one quarter to one third the heart attack rate of the surrounding towns. To make it even more remarkable, these men and women are overweight, especially the older men who are up to 80 pounds over the national average. Even more, the daily calorie intake is 3000 for men and 2300 for women, again above the national average. Even more, most of these calories come from animal fat. This is a puzzler, a miracle town, when we consider the fact that the nation's leading nutritionists, experts on diet, overweight, and heart disease, believe that the saturated animal fats and high caloric diet are major causes of heart attacks.

The explanation may well be the absence of emotional stress. The medical team investigating Roseto reported that the most striking feature of Roseto was the way in which the people seemed to enjoy life. They were gay, boisterous, and unpretentious. The wealthy dressed and behaved in ways similar to their less fortunate neighbors.

The people are further described as "simple, warm and very hospitable." There is said to be no crime in Roseto. The people are mutually trusting and mutually supporting. There is no real want since neighbors provide for the needy.

There we may well have the answer—the absence of anxiety and stress, the presence of simplicity, happiness, and an active life in which men and women work, even when they don't need the money.

And it is right here that we have the key to control of all psychosomatic health wreckers in all parts of the body. Worry and fear are the killers. Since worry and fear originate in the mind, in response to the anxious past and the troubled present, we must find and destroy these worries and fears before they destroy us.

You do this by searching your life patterns from the very beginning with the Conflict Check Chart, the outlined life story, the family history of fears and fatalities. Once you have found your worries and fears—*face them*. You disarm or explode them harmlessly under controlled conditions by using Guided Association, Relaxation therapy, and Substitute Aggression treatment (all detailed in Chapter 5). When you have done this you achieve serenity—the lesson of Roseto.

By the time you read this book, the younger people of Roseto will have left to join the stress- and anxiety-ridden "outer world" that you and I live in every day of our lives. The older inhabitants will live out their lives. And so we come to the ultimate realization that we must each of us find our own Roseto within our own minds and hearts. Just like the mythical Shangri-La and the Fountain of Youth, Roseto can only be found within ourselves. *This book teaches you how.*

Tobacco death

Another major cause of heart disease, especially coronary spasms and thrombosis, appears to be tobacco. The cigarette is probably the major offender. It is obvious that the person who is a chain smoker is suffering from a basic anxiety. But even more than that, nicotine causes spasm of blood vessels. Spasm of already narrowed coronary arteries can lead to clotting and complete closure, with death of the heart muscle. Many years ago I wrote a book entitled *Cancer Can Be Cured*. In this book I devoted four chapters to tobacco, and pointed out the relationship between cigarette smoking and cancer of the lung.

The case of Mrs. S. T. is a good example of a tobacco- and coffee-induced, anxious heart problem: She was a 23-year-old housewife, complained of insomnia, a "pressure over my heart whenever I do housecleaning," and a continuing sense of weakness and increasing "tired" feelings. Both her mother and father had died of heart disease in their late fifties. One brother had also died of a "heart attack" at 43 years of age.

Her obvious anxiety over her heart condition, resulting from this tragic family history, combined with the lack of sleep and her basic emotional stress of an early marriage at 17, were sufficient to cause her symptoms. There was no organic basis found, although she went to three cardiologists in addition to her family physician. To make matters worse, she was a chain smoker and drank "uncounted numbers of cups of coffee every day."

It was difficult to reassure this patient that she had no heart disease. Fortunately, when she stopped both coffee and tobacco, her symptoms were greatly relieved. It was obvious that we had been dealing with a vicious cycle of tobacco causing blood vessel spasm, coffee causing excessive stimulation of the central nervous system and preventing sleep, and the anxiety and natural fear of her family history aggravating both her tobacco and coffee habits. This chain of events was broken by reassurance, by the elimination of coffee and tobacco, and by Guided Association therapy to rid her of the repressed, emotional dynamite connected with the death of her mother, her father, and her brother.

Exercise in moderation—and learn to relax

Inadequate exercise is also a factor in predisposing all of us to coronary artery disease. I am personally opposed to competitive exercise, except for the professional athlete. This rules out golf and tennis, unless you can wander about the golf course, hitting the golf ball to release your aggressions, and not keeping score. Tennis is a very demanding, competitive sport. Unless you play every day, and have for years, you should not attempt this game for the first time if you are beyond 40 years of age.

Moderate, mild, daily exercise such as walking from one-half to one hour, perhaps before breakfast if convenient, is a very effective safeguard. Dr. Paul Dudley White, the eminent heart specialist, recommends daily bicycle riding to keep heart and other muscles in trim. I am in favor of such non-competitive, leisurely, pleasurable exercise. There is ample evidence that people who do such exercise have a decreased tendency to heart disease when compared to the completely sedentary individual.*

And finally, you must learn how to relax if you are to keep your heart and blood vessels in the best possible condition. You have already learned various methods to help you relax both mind and body (Chapter 5), and you should practice daily, both while at work and at rest.

---

* Earl L. Wallis and Gene A. Logan, *Isometric Exercises* (Englewood Cliffs: Prentice-Hall), offers useful no-movement exercises.

Heredity and your heart

And now a word about your genetic constitution. This is unpredictable and unknowable. Your parents may have died of heart disease, and, yet, you yourself may have no genetic predisposition to such conditions. Human heredity is very complex. However, if there is a history of heart conditions within your family, it is best to see your physician for a careful examination. He will give you the reassurance and guidance you need. Since this is an element none of us can control, there is no point in further discussion. Keep yourself in the best possible physical condition, exercise as described above, watch your diet carefully, and avoid stress and tobacco. These are the major elements, regardless of your genetic constitution.

The anxious heart speaks

How can you recognize the anxious heart? Organ language is the answer, and, of course, the basic underlying anxiety that goes with all psychosomatic problems. You should know yourself well enough to know whether or not anxiety is part of your problem. You know whether or not financial problems, your home, your job, your husband, wife, or children are placing unbearable stress upon you.

When we add to this the organ language of palpitations (awareness of the heart beat), a rapid heart rate, pounding in the chest or in the ears, chest pain or other discomfort in the heart region, and perhaps shortness of breath and fatigue, we have the evidences of the anxious heart. This is sometimes called "effort syndrome," because the discomfort may come on when you exert yourself. However, since such chest pains and other symptoms may also be due to organic heart disease, you must always consult your physician and not depend on your own diagnostic abilities. He will do a careful study, using the electrocardiogram for study of the electrical impulses coming from the heart, X-ray your heart and lungs, and perhaps your intestinal tract. He will consider the possibility of tobacco poisoning, rupture of the diaphragm, gall bladder or ulcer disease, neuralgia, spinal disease, and so forth. Obviously, you cannot make this differential diagnosis yourself.

However, once your physician has ruled out organic disease and has confirmed your impression of the anxious heart, you will be in a position to help your physician make yourself well. You will be in a position, literally, to "heal thyself."

How to treat the anxious heart

In the first place, you must insist on a definite statement from your physician. Ask for a positive "yes" or "no" in answer to the question, "do I have heart disease?" A capable cardiologist will be able to answer this question in a very definite fashion in practically every case. If there is an organic condition, place yourself under his care. If there is not, thank him, say good-bye, and lead a normal life.

If your condition is an anxious heart, you don't need drugs. Certainly, you don't need any medicine for your heart. You may need a mild barbiturate to tide you over the interim anxiety state until you can bring things under control in a more definitive fashion.

Very few patients need a psychiatrist to help them control their anxieties. In most cases the techniques described in Chapter 5, and particularly the relaxation therapy methods with affirmative Self-Suggestion for self-control of the mind-body unit will provide the best form of self-therapy.

Study the Conflict Check Chart (Chapter 4) fill it out honestly and carefully, and you will learn the major areas of anxiety in your life. Now, apply the Guided Association therapy method as described in Chapter 5 to release the repressed emotional dynamite that has been causing your basic anxiety. Guided Association, combined with relaxation therapy and affirmative Self-Suggestion, will give you a sense of release, freedom from fear and tension, and a completely revitalized capacity to handle all your anxiety problems, including those of the anxious heart. Your symptoms will rapidly come under control and will soon disappear.

Points to remember:

1. Heart disease is our number one killer, *but*
2. Most heart region (left chest) pain is not organic.

3. Coronary disease is a SEDENTARY problem:

S	Stress
E	Emotion
D	Diet
E	Exercise (deficiency or competitive)
N	Neuro-psychic
T	Tobacco
A	Anxiety
R	Relaxation resistance
Y	You (your genetic structure)

4. Not all pain is heart pain.
5. When your heart "speaks" (organ language), you must listen.
6. Your heart may be saying—"organic!" or "anxiety is the cause" or "misinterpretation of your physician's statements."
7. The happy heart is the healthy heart.
8. Learn to be happy, to treat serious things lightly and light things seriously.
9. Stop smoking.
   Stop coffee.
   Stay on Dr. Cantor's Diet (*See* Chapter 8, p. 139).
10. Learn to relax (*See* Chapter 5).

Chapter 8

OBESITY, ITS CAUSES AND CURE

How to use chapter 8

1. Check this list and see if you have any of the following symptoms:

   YOU ARE OVERWEIGHT (*See* Weight Tables, page 149).

   Excess weight with any or all of the following—Heart symptoms such as pain after exertion, shortness of breath, chest discomfort, swollen ankles.

   Rupture.

   Diabetes symptoms such as continuous hunger, thirst, frequent urination.

   Arthritis.

   Kidney symptoms such as frequent urination, puffy eyes in the morning.

   Compulsive eating, even between meals.

   You tire easily and have little pep.

   You look older than you should for your age group.

2. If you are too fat—with or without any of the above symptoms, read this chapter NOW.

3. Then, turn back to Chapter 4 and fill out the Conflict Check Chart.

   This will tell you *why* you are overweight.

4. Now, turn to Chapter 5 and use the Guided Association home sessions to get rid of your emotional problems.

5. Practice the Self-Suggestion methods to control your eating compulsions.

How to escape from your fortress of fat

So you want to lose weight! That is very wise. Excess fat may predispose you to diabetes, heart disease, strokes, arthritis, kidney trouble, hernia, postural deformities, and many other diseases—perhaps even cancer. It may very well shorten your life. When you lose weight, you will add years to your life, and life to your years.

In most cases the overweight patient is a problem in psychosomatic medicine and nutrition. Most of us who carry excess pounds simply overeat, and we overeat because of emotional problems. On the other hand, there are some who are overweight because of one additional factor—a lazy thyroid.

The lazy thyroid can develop at any age, but hovers in the background of most obesity cases that are beyond 40 years of age. Unless the thyroid gland is secreting a normal amount of its important hormone, the body puts on weight even if you are not overeating. Fortunately, there is a simple blood test to determine thyroid function, and you will learn more about this later in this chapter.

Whether you know it or not, overeating is usually evidence of anxiety. In most cases the anxiety is in your subconscious mind, and you are not aware of it. In this section we will discuss some of the basic problems related to overeating. You have already learned the general background of all anxiety in Chapter 5 and Chapter 3, when you reviewed your own Conflict Check Chart.

On the other hand, you may be well aware of your troubles at home, in business, or within yourself. Whether or not you are now aware of them, you will be before completing this important chapter. The psychosomatic approach to obesity provides the help you need in the simplest possible fashion. You will overcome your emotional problems, and shed the unwanted pounds. You will actually develop an entirely new personality and become a happier and healthier person. Best of all, you will accomplish all of this in a relatively short time.

Once you have overcome the *need* to be fat, it will be a relatively simple matter to achieve and maintain your new face and figure, even without drugs. If you need medications to assist you in controlling your appetite, or for the management of a sluggish thyroid gland, your physician will advise you. Naturally, you will not start on any serious reducing routine without medical help. However, the important point is that the major control must always come from within yourself. Unless you develop such control, using the methods described in this book, you will soon return to your flabby figure. You will regain fat even though you may still be taking appetite-depressant drugs. After all, you should not continue to take drugs forever. It is not necessary, and it is dangerous. What you do need is to learn the truth, about obesity and about yourself, and the truth will set you free from your fortress of fat.

Molly M., 20 years of age, illustrates some of these points. She was unmarried, had no dates, and probably would remain without a husband as long as she retained her enormous, flabby fat. She was shapeless, over 70 pounds beyond the normal weight. She was convinced that she would never marry. Her mother brought her to me in despair. "Who would want to marry me," wailed the youngster. It was a good question, and the only answer I could give her was that it would have to be someone more overweight than she was.

However, if she really wanted to lose weight, I told her that it probably could be done. But, I warned, she must desperately *want* to lose weight.

The study of this girl's Conflict Check Chart revealed many problem areas. She had some very curious ideas about the opposite sex and about the sex act. She feared being touched by men. She hated both her father and her mother because "they sleep in the same bed." She hated an older sister who was married and six months pregnant.

This youngster required extensive re-education, accomplished partially during consultations and partially by advising appropriate reading matter. One office consultation required both mother and father to be present so that they could better understand the special emotional problems involved. Molly's emotional problem was basically fear of the opposite sex. She was afraid of sex itself, and of marriage. She was using her fortress of fat as an excuse for staying away from men. She knew that no man would be attracted to her if she was fat, flabby, and shapeless. This was her defense against a normal life. This was the emotionally-based reason for her excess weight. The Conflict Check Chart brought this fear into the open. Guided Association helped Molly root out these unnatural fears.

The weight loss was gradual, but the ultimate result was good. The personality change was especially striking, and a remarkably transformed slim butterfly emerged from the flabby cocoon.

You and your conflicts

Let us assume that you are overweight because you eat too much. It is very simple to say, "eat less." It is very difficult to do this if there are underlying emotional pressures forcing you to stuff food into your mouth.

The important thing is to find out why you eat so much. The plain truth is that overeating is an immature reaction. When you are under stress, you reach for food instead of a solution to your problem. When you are unhappy, you put things into your mouth exactly as you did when you were a child.

This is a natural thing to do. Our safe haven as a baby was mother's nipple. At the breast, we felt secure, and food became equated with security from infancy on. This continued through the gamut of foods, mother and dad demonstrating their love for us by feeding us when we could not eat for ourselves, and urging us to eat more when we could manipulate our own knives and forks. Later came cigarettes, pipes, or cigars, a further evidence of the need to put things in our mouths during times of stress and strain, insecurity, or unhappiness.

Family patterns

Mrs. R.L., 32 years of age, had "always been fat." She needed to lose 50 pounds, as evidenced by comparison of her height, weight, and body structure with the statistical norms of the modern weight tables (*See* Page 149). Her family had always eaten well. They were devoted to good food, and her mother had always said, "even if we must stint on other things, we will never stint on food."

The family dining room table carried both quality and quantity, and the children were urged to eat. Her mother always said, "eat well and you will be well." This left her and her three brothers with a feeling that if they did not eat well, the reverse would be true and they would suffer illness. Accordingly, they were all very stout from childhood on.

It is important to check on family eating patterns in all cases. Overeating as a result of your childhood training may be an important factor in your own problem. However, in this case the eating pattern was only part of the problem. The protein-bound iodine test of her blood showed a sluggish thyroid. Even if Mrs. R.L. had been placed on a very low caloric diet, she would not have lost weight. This was borne out by the fact that she had been to a number of "obesity specialists" who had treated her with the usual selection of multicolored pills. She had taken these pills regularly, several times a day, before and after meals, as instructed. However, she did not lose weight and continued to gain. Furthermore, the amphetamine content of these drugs made her very jittery, and she could not sleep.

Once, while driving, she almost had an accident. She believed that this was due to the "jittery nerves" that she had "while taking those diet pills." This is a very common experience. Because of the lazy thyroid—in addition to the recognition of her family habit pattern—the key to reducing was the use of the tiny, thyroid analog pills.

When placed on the proper medication, in the proper dosage, and the proper diet (*See* Page 139), her body fat almost literally melted away. During this process, the safflower oil cocktail (*See* Page 147) helped change her body fat to a more unsaturated, soft fat, allowing for weight loss without premature wrinkling and aging. She retained the soft, rounded contours of youth while losing the ugly flabbiness of excess fat.

Her weight loss the first week was over nine pounds, and she thereafter stabilized at a loss of approximately two or three pounds per week until the required optimal weight level was reached.

This patient illustrates the ideal approach to the psychosomatic problem. We must treat our body and mind as a single unit—the body-mind. We do this by discovering what part of our symptoms is due to "mind" (emotionally-based worry and fear) and what part is due to actual body changes. In this case the emotional drive originated in her family pressure to overeat and in her mother's "command" to "eat well and you will be well." Her family history and the Conflict Check Chart brought this into the open.

Guided Association helped her to recognize the strong emotions of fear of illness and death that her mother had implanted with the command to "eat well and you will be well." She relived these times of misguided mother love to the point of boredom and laughter when she finally realized "how wrong mother was."

Once released from this "command," she used the affirmation patterns of this chapter (Page 132) to change her thinking and behaviour at the dinner table.

The "body" fraction of her psychosomatic problem was the sluggish thyroid. This was recognized and corrected. The combined body-mind treatment of the combined body-mind problem conquered her psychosomatic health-wrecker.

In many cases of obesity there is a body factor, most often this very same sluggish thyroid. In some cases there is only an emotionally-compulsive overeating. The Conflict Check Chart is essential to locate the emotional factors. Guided Association and the other methods of Chapter 5 and of this chapter are essential to rid yourself of these emotional weeds in your mind.

We are all immature

You may find it hard to believe that you are one of a group of immature people, very much like the alcoholic or the drug addict. But since you must supply an answer to your emotional need by food and more food, you are an addict in a very real sense. The alcoholic needs alcohol and the drug addict needs more and more narcotics. You "need" food.

But you are not alone. We are all addicts to one thing or another. We are all immature to some degree. No one ever achieves full maturity, whether he is the average person, a psychiatrist or a genius. Indeed, the higher the level of your intelligence the greater the probability that you have many areas in which you are quite immature. The more intelligent you are, the more sensitive you are to the world about you. So it is not surprising that you react in an emotional way to unhappiness, disease, death, and destruction that you see in modern society.

But, in your case, you must remember that you really don't *need* the excess food. As a matter of fact, we would all live a great deal longer if we ate a very simple diet. You may be surprised to learn that a single tin of sardines each day will supply all your food requirements. You may need to supplement this with a well rounded vitamin-mineral tablet, but that's all. We can go a step further and tell you that you will live longer if you stay on this diet than you would on almost any other. A little later on I will tell you about the longevity diet.

Since your apparent *need* for food is psychological, it is obviously a reaction to a difficult or unhappy life situation. Stop stuffing food into your mouth instead of ideas into your mind. You must learn to react on a more mature level, in terms of the needs of your problem situation, rather than regressing to your mother's breast, your baby (alcohol) bottle, your thumb (cigarette or cigar sucking), your habit of stuffing food into your mouth.

Once you recognize the fact that you are a compulsive eater, the problem is half-cured. The next step is to locate your areas of immaturity and get rid of the unconscious compulsion to overeat.

Please remember that we are all immature. We all feel insecure. Please remember that I am not criticizing your reactions, but merely describing them. Working together, as detailed particularly in Chapters 3, 4 and 5, we can overcome your unconscious compulsion to overeat. And we will.

Why you should lose weight

You should lose weight for the following reasons:

1. You will look better with a slimmer figure.
2. You will be generally healthier.
3. You will live longer.
4. You will be much less likely to develop heart disease, a hemorrhage in your brain, diabetes, arthritis, kidney trouble, and many other diseases.
5. You will develop a more mature, more relaxed, more controlled personality.
6. You will have greater vitality.
7. You will be easier to live with.
8. You will be the envy of your fat friends.

We are all trying to commit suicide in one way or another. Some of us do it by overwork, some by too much alcohol, others by drugs or sexual dissipation. You may have been doing it by overeating. This is a slow bullet, a bullet that will ultimately reach a vital spot just as surely as if you held a gun to your head and pulled the trigger. Recognize this, and recognize the advantages of losing weight, and you have the answer to the question—"Why should I lose weight?"

What is maturity

Go back right now to Chapter 2 for a complete discussion of maturity, immaturity, and how your personality influences your health. Right now, it is important for you to recognize that complete maturity in all things is impossible. We can be certain that, at least in the matter of overeating, the very fact that you are overweight indicates that you are immature. Whether your problems are in the sexual, physical, financial, or other spheres, if you react by stuffing food into your mouth, you are immature. That is not the way to solve your problems.

I cannot solve your problems for you. I can, however, help you to recognize your general areas of immaturity, and help you to overcome your childish forms of behavior. You have already started in this direction when you filled out the Conflict Check Chart, and perhaps when you began your Guided Association sessions. During the process of correcting the various problems located by your Conflict Check Chart, you will produce a complete change in your personality. You will correct many areas of immaturity, including those that cause you to overeat. As you become more mature in your eating habits, you will at the same time increase your maturity level in your other habits. Eating is never an isolated evidence of immaturity. You are undoubtedly childish in many of your other reactions.

The fat of ambition

John W. was 52 years of age and the president of his company. He had come up the hard way, with very little formal education, never having graduated high school. His family consisted only of his father and himself, his mother having died during childbirth. His father had never been successful, and this resulted in an unusual ambition and drive in the youngster.

Living alone as they did, there was very little attention paid to food. Both father and son ate relatively little, and very little cooking was done. John felt that if he were ever successful, he would eat only the finest foods in the finest restaurants. This he did. He was so successful that he became very obese and carried his paunch proudly as evidence of his success.

John did not marry and continued his habit of eating in fine restaurants. He particularly enjoyed French food and the rich sauces that went with such food. When he began to develop high blood pressure, shortness of breath, and found that he tired easily, he consulted a physician. Indeed, he went from one physician to another, searching for someone who would tell him he could eat whatever he wanted and still lose weight. He finally found one such physician who did not believe in calories. However, his weight remained stable and even increased slightly.

My own study revealed a very high blood pressure, a high blood-cholesterol level, early evidences of heart failure, evidence of hardening of the arteries, a weight excess of 63 pounds, and excess smoking and alcohol drinking as well as excess food intake.

His blood studies showed a lazy thyroid as well as the excess cholesterol level and some evidence of poor kidney function. The patient was advised that he must lose weight or die much earlier than he might otherwise pass on. The evidence was presented to him, along with the statistics on his condition as it related to coronary artery disease, stroke, and death at a relatively early age. John was a very intelligent man, and this provided sufficient motivation.

In my experience there are two major areas of motivation: (1) appearance, which is important to both sexes, but especially the female; and (2) the desire to stay alive. Both elements are active in practically every overweight patient who seeks help. In this case it was primarily the desire to stay alive that started John on the right track. The use of the tiny, thyroid analog pills, combined with the correct diet, and Guided Association to eliminate various emotional factors in the background relating to his childhood and his drive for status and wealth, resulted in gradual slimming at the ideal rate of approximately two pounds per week.

Don't take dangerous drugs

A word of caution before we go further. If you are the average, overweight patient, you have already been to see one or more physicians. You have probably been taking appetite-depressant drugs, drugs containing amphetamine. This is a central nervous system stimulant that does depress appetite. However, it may make you very jittery, may raise your blood pressure, and may actually start you on a drug habit. You may get to like the feeling of nervous system excitation. You will then be "hooked" on amphetamine just as surely as the narcotic addict is "hooked" on his "fix."

You may lose a certain amount of weight, but you will not have changed or even touched the *causes* of your overeating. Obviously, until you remove the causes, you cannot cure the basic problem. It is very much like taking aspirin for a headache. If the headache is due to a brain tumor, it would take a lot of aspirin to get rid of the headache. But you will still have a brain tumor. The only way to really cure that headache is to remove the brain tumor.

The same thing is true of your overeating habit. If you take enough drugs, you may suppress your appetite. You may lose a certain amount of weight. But the basic immaturity that made you overeat in the first place remains. When you stop taking the drugs, you will once again begin to eat too much. You will once again regain your weight, and perhaps even more.

How to become less childish and lose weight

You know now that overeating is childish. You understand its origin in your early childhood and know that food represents a substitute for love and provides a sense of security. But you also know the great dangers of obesity. Now you want to grow up, to act your age, to stop overeating What do you do? Your procedure will be as follows:

1. Complete the Conflict Check Chart.
2. Work through the problem areas with Guided Association until you have rid yourself of your repressed emotional dynamite. When you have done this to the point of boredom or

laughter, with every one of these trouble spots, you may proceed to the next step.

3. Now practice the relaxation methods until you have achieved complete mastery of voluntary muscle relaxation. While in this state of complete relaxation practice the Self-Suggestion methods to be described a little later in this chapter.

4. Follow the simple diet rules and drink the amazing Cantor Cocktail. Both the low carbohydrate, high protein, low fat gourmet diet (Page 139) and the Cocktail will help you change your solid fat to soft fat and to redistribute your body fat to produce rounded, firm curves.

But before you start any routine, you must consult your physician. Make sure that he does a protein-bound iodine blood test. This simple test determines the function of your thyroid gland. If you are suffering from a lazy thyroid, he will give you tiny, thyroid analog pills, perhaps one or two a day, to restore your metabolism to a normal level. If his examination reveals any other physical or functional abnormalities, they will have to be corrected. You may then safely proceed with the four steps to a slim, trim figure, as above outlined. The combination will give you the long-lasting result you want.

Develop better habit patterns

Develop the habit of *minimal expectations*. Do not expect too much from yourself and do not expect too much from others. If you expect too much from yourself, you are apt to become frustrated. You may develop an anxiety state that will cause even more than obesity. Set your sights high but make your goals realistic. You need not aim for the presidency of your corporation. You need not be a millionaire. You need not be a movie star. You need not be President of the United States. If you make your goals realistic, and set your sights on the simple life, you will be much happier. *Learn to be content* with what you have and what you are. There is a very ancient saying that the man who is content with what he has is truly rich.

And *don't look back*. Don't destroy the happiness of the present moment—the only moment you will ever have—by thinking about what might have been. Lot's wife looked back and then turned into a pillar of salt. Don't do that. I am not telling you to kill all ambition. I am merely telling you to set realistic goals. Meanwhile, learn to be content with the amount of money you have, the home you have, your job, your family. You will be happier, and you will not need to drown your sorrows in alcohol or hide behind a fortress of fat.

And don't expect too much from your associates, your wife, your children. They are just as human as you are. They also have their levels of immaturity. Don't expect your spouse to be the movie version of the great lover. Don't demand perfection of yourself and don't demand it of others.

Learn to accept the things you cannot change and correct the bad habits that can be changed. Minimal expectations, realistic goals, contentment with what you have, acceptance of that which cannot be changed, hard work to change controllable problems—will all add up to the development of new habits of thinking and behaviour.

The teenager "fatty"

Many teenagers are overweight. These are often difficult problem cases. It is surprising, however, how many of them are victims of a lazy thyroid gland. The ordinary basal metabolism test may not be sufficiently accurate to show evidences of a minimal deviation from the normal. And yet it is this very mild deviation from normal that makes it practically impossible for these youngsters to lose weight, even on a very low caloric diet. It must always be remembered, however, that the key to weight loss rests with careful study, the correction of any metabolic defect, a low caloric diet, proper motivation, and elimination of background emotional problems.

Mary Ellen was a case in point. The simple, protein-bound iodine blood test showed evidence of a sluggish thyroid. Her Conflict Check Chart revealed many emotionally disturbing situations in her home and school background. She did not get along with the other children at school, and although she was very bright, she rebelled against her teachers. Indeed, she was too bright for the level of her class and rapidly lost interest in the work. Her teachers thought she was daydreaming and uninterested because she didn't like the work or the teacher, and she was punished accordingly.

At home, her mother, who was very slim and attractive and even looked younger than her own daughter, continually berated her for overeating, for raiding the icebox, for T.V. snacks, and, of course, for her very poor school work. Her mother was advised that she must change her attitude toward her daughter if her daughter was to ever lose weight successfully and permanently. Being intelligent, and recognizing the competition she presented to her own daughter (competition for her husband's affection as well as generally), she re-oriented her own thinking and her own behaviour toward the girl.

Consultation with the youngster's guidance teacher showed that she had a superior intelligence quotient (I.Q.), and probably was not interested in her school work because she was not sufficiently stimulated by it. She needed more advanced work and individual attention. She particularly needed this personal attention since she felt herself an outcast, hiding within her own fortress of fat.

Changes in the environmental situation, combined with Guided Association and thyroid analog tablets, finally broke the fat barrier. She began to lose weight and showed a remarkable change in personality. She soon attained the required 40 pound weight loss, and became an entirely different person. She literally zoomed into the cheerleading squad and was one of the most attractive girls in her school.

How to substitute good habits for bad

The next step is to learn to substitute good habits, good emotions, good attitudes, for your present poor ones. One of your bad habits, of course, is overeating. You now know that when you are consciously or unconsciously insecure, unhappy, and feel unloved or unwanted, you overeat and overdrink.

When you take a few cocktails before dinner, a brandy after dinner, and eat a seven course meal, you are not exactly hitting the bottle, but you are certainly taking the immature route to a childish escape from reality. You can escape only temporarily by numbing your brain with alcohol. You can escape only temporarily by regressing to your childhood habit of stuffing food into your mouth. In time you will need more and more food and more and more alcohol. The problem eater becomes a fatty cripple, and the social drinker becomes a true alcoholic. If you are heading in that direction, stop now.

Change your habits of eating and drinking. *Develop the habit of courage,* the courage to face the facts of life. Learn to make the best of everything. Have the courage, however, to change the things you can change. Set realistic goals and work toward them. Have the courage to stick to your goals, and you will usually succeed. The important thing is trying. Give your efforts the best you can. That is the kind of courage I want you to develop.

To develop this kind of courage, you will need to practice the good habit and the good attitude of *determination.* When you set realistic goals, develop the determination that you will reach those goals. Develop this determination in all areas of your life. Take the attitude that you have not yet begun to fight. Stick to your goal, and have faith.

There is a special courage that comes from faith, *faith in yourself and faith in God.* When you make God your partner, you will be working with a power greater than yourself. You will increase your strength and your courage tremendously. And remember the Biblical admonition, "He that endureth to the end shall be saved."

Develop the attitude of *enthusiasm. Be cheerful* at all times. This is a good attitude, a good habit to carry with you throughout life. Remember that life is a journey, and we are all headed for the same destination. The important thing is to slow down a bit and enjoy the scenery, one moment, one day at a time. Since none of us will get out of this world alive, let's take our time on this trip, and let's determine to enjoy every moment of it. Slow down, enjoy life right now, have fun, get rid of your frustrations and anxieties, and *be cheerful all the time.* Do everything with enthusiasm, and you will do it better. Best of all, you will have fun while doing it.

When you practice your Self-Suggestion Technique (*See* Chapter 5), use the appropriate self-suggestions to substitute good eating and thinking habits for your present immature behaviour patterns.

How to practice self-suggestion to overcome obesity

Self-Suggestion is one of the best ways to change your attitudes and habits. By Self-Suggestion, you can rapidly substitute good emotions for bad emotions, and good behavior patterns for childish forms of behaviour, the poor habit patterns you are now living with. The new attitudes and habits will allow you to develop a new set of deep emotions. What may start off as superficial happiness, enthusiasm and determination, will in time become your natural self.

You are what you eat and what you think. Remember that. It is because of that fact that Self-Suggestion is so effective in remoulding your personality and character.

Self-suggestion and Guided Association in action

Mrs. Rose E. hated her husband. She thought that her husband hated her. Actually, he had lost interest in her because she had become fat, flabby, and old before her time. "She is no longer the girl I married," said Mr. E. She had indeed become a shrew. This was a vicious circle, the wife hating her husband because she thought he had lost interest in her, and her husband had indeed lost interest because she had let herself go, overeating constantly, being especially addicted to T.V. snacks and rich desserts. She "adored" cake and ice cream and often had this combination as dessert and while shopping.

Her blood studies showed a high blood cholesterol level, not surprising with her diet. But her thyroid function was quite normal. All her other tests showed a normal metabolism and normal organ functions. She had neither high blood pressure nor heart disease.

In this case we were dealing with a problem in motivation. It was necessary to break the vicious cycle of hostility within the husband-wife relationship. This is very often difficult, since it involves two people, only one of whom is the patient. In such cases it is essential to discuss the matter with the husband. If he is cooperative, the problem is more easily resolved. If he is not willing to help, it may be essential for the patient to develop other interests away from home. In most cases I have seen, divorce has not been necessary.

It was pointed out to the overweight wife that her husband would regain his interest in her if she became slim and attractive. If she became sufficiently slim and attractive in her appearance to capture the attention of other men, the natural jealousy and possessiveness of a husband would reassert itself. When she recognized this fact, she rose to the challenge.

Self-Suggestion was most important in her treatment. She had to change her attitudes and her habits as well as her emotions. Guided Association released her enormous hostility toward her husband. She soon recognized that his hostility and her own were both based upon her own poor eating habits and the fact that she had lost the slim figure that had originally attracted her husband. Change in diet habit being properly motivated, she soon lost one to three pounds each week. In time she became both slimmer and more attractive.

As her hostility disappeared, her personality and behaviour patterns improved, and her husband's reaction was all that could be desired. No marriage runs smoothly all the time, but considering the circumstances at the beginning of this problem, the results were almost miraculous.

More helpful words for self-suggestion

In Chapter 5 you learned the basic importance of suggestion therapy in all psychosomatic problems. You now know that it is the key to long-term weight loss. Go back to that fundamental chapter to reread and practice the methods for deep relaxation, for commands to the unconscious mind, and for the waking command that continues to act 24 hours a day, day after day. Practice the method of key-word, rapid Self-Suggestion and the reinforcement techniques. When you have become expert in the positive approach, you will be able to cope with the irrational general anxiety that is in the background of all psychosomatic problems. You will be able to develop new habits of thinking and behaviour, as well as new deep-seated, positive emotions. You will be able to handle criticism better. You will begin to enjoy living in general, marriage, sex, and you will be more fun to be with.

The helpful words for self-suggestion in ridding yourself of excess fat include *slimmer and slimmer, thinner and thinner, calm and cheerful, happier and happier, healthier and healthier, younger and younger.*

The key phrase is *every day, in every way, I am getting slimmer and slimmer.* You may follow this by any of the other key words and phrases you may choose.

Self-Suggestion can be practiced all day long, no matter what you are doing. It will be most effective, however, if you use it when you are fully relaxed, preferably just before falling off to sleep. So place yourself in a state of complete relaxation as often as possible throughout the day, and certainly at bedtime, using the relaxation methods you have already learned. And when you are fully relaxed you may make the following suggestions to yourself, depending upon your objectives.

For weight-loss say the following: *Every day, in every way, I am eating less and less.* Or, *Slimmer and slimmer, with the Cantor diet.*

A good self-suggestion is:

Every cell, every tissue, every organ of my body is becoming healthier and healthier, happier and happier, and I am becoming thinner and thinner, every day, in every way.

Remember that your body will follow and accept these self-suggestions to make them a fact. *You need not instruct your body how to do it.* You will actually become thinner and thinner, healthier and healthier, every day, in every way. You will become happier and happier with each passing day.

In this way, using the appropriate self-suggestions, you can make yourself more enthusiastic, calmer, more generous, or more determined and more courageous than you are right now. You may use self-suggestions to develop the habit of sincerity and honesty. You must *become honest enough to accept responsibility for your own troubles.* When you become honest enough with yourself to realize that everything bad that has happened to you throughout your entire life—including your excess fat—is your own fault, you will have taken a giant step forward toward true maturity.

Group therapy helps

It has been my experience that these methods work best for the overweight if you practice them in the company of others—

friends, neighbors, relatives, or a group of overweight people. I would suggest that you arrange weekly meetings, for the discussion and practice of relaxation and self-suggestion. Choose a group leader for this purpose.

Your plan should be to read a chapter of this book and then discuss it before beginning the relaxation session. You will then all go on to complete relaxation, followed by the appropriate self-suggestions. Perhaps your physician will help you set up such a group to meet in his office or in your home.

These discussion groups help to bring out many new points. Your experience and the experience of others will be helpful to each of you. The healthy spirit of competition in a group helps you all to remain on your diet, and to reduce your weight. You will see your friends and neighbors growing younger, slimmer, happier, and healthier before your very eyes. They will see the same miracle taking place in you.

The magic diet

And now we come at last to the magic diet. It is quite a gourmet diet. You will not starve. Indeed, you must eat three meals each day, and you may even eat between meals.

You may eat the following in any amount—even between meals:

1. Lean meat (steaks, chops, etc.).
2. Seafood. Fish every day is a good rule for a slim figure and a long life.
3. All vegetables *except* potatoes, corn, rice, beans (*but* you may have string beans). Use lemon juice or vinegar and safflower or corn oil as a dressing on vegetable salads.
4. Orange, grapefruit, or melon. Start and finish your meals with one of these fruits.
5. Clear bouillon, or freshly squeezed vegetable juices.
6. Hard cooked egg white. Do not use the yolks and avoid the fat and cholesterol.
7. For between-meal snacks—tomato and lean meat, cottage cheese or farmer cheese.
8. For your drink—unsweetened tea or coffee, or low caloric soda, BUT *You will lose weight most rapidly if you avoid liquids before, during, and for two hours after meals.*

Avoid:

1. Fried foods, unless fried in safflower oil.
2. Saturated fats (all hard fats, solid at room temperature).
3. No butter, but corn or safflower oil margarine is okay.
4. Bread, potatoes, rice, corn, peas, and all beans, except string beans.
5. All fruit except orange, grapefruit or melon.
6. Cereals.
7. Liquor.
8. Ordinary soft drinks (low caloric drinks are okay).

Here is the actual set of diet instructions as they are presented to my overweight patients. You will find a detailed REDUCE AND STAY REDUCED DIET, and the instructions for preparation of the Cantor Cocktail.

You will also find the LUCKY ELEVEN rules for a slimmer figure.

This is the amazing and original, medically approved REDUCE AND STAY REDUCED DIET. It will help you to:

1. Reduce your excess weight.
2. Remove cholesterol deposits from your arteries.
3. Restore more youthful contours to your body.

The REDUCE AND STAY REDUCED DIET is a diet pattern based on vegetable oil foods, low in animal fat but high in liquid vegetable oil. Animal fats are reduced by omitting food containing butter fat and egg yolks; by substituting lean meat; by using low-fat cookery; and by selecting low-fat foods.

Liquid vegetable oils are used for shortening when cooking and baking and when preparing dressings and sauces. Of course, you will do little or no baking, and you will use no sauces, anyhow, since you want to rid yourself of those excess pounds. But if someone in your family is not overweight, you may want to use healthful sauces and baked foods for better heart and blood vessel health. Oils must replace margarine, lard, and butter. The special margarines made with the polyunsaturated corn or safflower oils are okay, but remember that *all fats, even the polyunsaturated oil fats, are high caloric and should not be taken in excess.*

To lower the fat in your blood, three things are very important:

1. Limit meat fat to 1 tablespoon (½ oz. or 15 grams) a day.
2. Use the corn or safflower oils in your salads each day and drink your safflower oil cocktail.
3. Lose excess weight, and *do not regain it.*

SPECIAL NOTE: Eat fish every day, if you can.

RECOMMENDED DAILY AMOUNTS OF FAT: (Safflower or Corn Oil Are The Best Sources for This Fat)

Sedentary women up to 68″ and 125 lbs.	4 tablespoons (2 ounces or ¼ cup)
Sedentary men and women up to 150 lbs.	5 tablespoons (2½ ounces or ⅓ cup, scant)
Active men and women up to 150 lbs.	6 tablespoons (3 ounces or ⅜ cup)
Men 72″ or more and/or more than 170 lbs.	7 tablespoons (3½ ounces or ½ cup, scant)

SPECIAL NOTE: If your physician tells you that you have a high level of blood cholesterol, you should be especially careful to take *as little animal fat as possible,* you should eat *as much fish as you can,* and you should *drink your safflower oil cocktail before each meal.*

SOURCES OF FAT TO BE AVOIDED

Bacon	Coconut
Butter	Cream
Hard cheese	Whole milk
Chicken fat	Salt pork
Chocolate	Egg yolk
Olive oil	Ice cream
Cocoa	Lard
Commercial shortenings	
Regular margarines	

Avoid all foods containing the above items

Avoid all the following cuts of meat:

Bacon	Prime rib roast
Club steak	Spareribs
Duck	

COOKING DIRECTIONS

SUBSTITUTIONS:

If recipe calls for:	*Use instead:*
1 egg yolk	1 egg white
1 whole egg	2 egg whites
2 eggs	3 egg whites
Cheese	Dry cottage cheese, or sapsago cheese for grating
Cream	Non-fat milk solids mixed to double or triple strength or evaporated skim milk

All obviously fatty cuts
of lamb and pork

Whole milk	Skim milk, buttermilk
Butter, regular margarine	Special margarine or vegetable oil

RESTAURANT MEALS

See "choose freely" foods

Salad dressing: vegetable oil and vinegar.

Fish or seafood: raw, broiled, boiled, or baked—with cocktail sauce, tartar sauce, or lemon.

No LIMIT

The following dishes provide 5 to 10 grams or less of animal fat in each 3 ounce serving:

Liver
Chicken: broiled (remove skin from chicken)—5 grams fat
Beef tenderloin: broiled—10 grams fat
Turkey: roasted or baked—omit gravy, skin and dressing —10 grams fat

To PREPARE MEATS:

Cut off excess fat before cooking.
Broil, roast, bake, boil. Foods may be cooked in vegetable oil. Cook meat on rack for proper fat drainage. Brown meat under broiler without adding fat. Soups and meat stock should always be refrigerated and the fat removed before serving. *Cut off all visible fat before eating meat.*

VEGETABLE OIL:

Suitable oils are: safflower, corn, soybean, or cottonseed
3 teaspoons equals 1 tablespoon
1 ounce equals 2 tablespoons
It is very important to use all of the oil prescribed.

SAMPLE MEAL PATTERN

BREAKFAST (No animal fat)
   Fruit—orange, grapefruit, or melon
   Profile-type bread toast (one slice)
      with corn oil or safflower oil margarine
   Whites of hard boiled eggs (as many as you want)
   Cottage, pot, or farmer's cheese (if you desire)
   Skimmed milk (preferably the vitamin-fortified type)—
      one glass
      or, coffee, with or without skimmed milk
      or, tea, with lemon or skimmed milk
      use a sugar substitute, if desired.

This is a hearty breakfast for anyone.

SPECIAL NOTE: You may drink your safflower oil cocktail *instead of the above* if you wish. It represents a full meal in itself. This is true for lunch and dinner as well, and is an especially effective method if you want to lose weight in a hurry.

    LUNCH (5 grams or less of animal fat)
        Fish or a serving of meat from the 5 gram list
        Vegetable
        Salad with vegetable oil dressing
        Coffee, tea, or skimmed milk—as at breakfast

This is a full and hearty lunch, for you may have as much fish as you wish, and a large, mixed, green and tomato vegetable salad with oil and vinegar (or lemon) dressing.

SPECIAL NOTE: Fish is better for you than meat. It contains important, health-giving minerals as well as very unsaturated fats.

    DINNER (10-15 grams of animal fat)
        Soup (fat removed)—bouillon is best
        Fish, meat, or substitute from the "Meat, Cheese, Poultry, and Eggs" List
        Vegetables
        Salad with vegetable oil dressing
        Profile-type bread toast—one slice with special margarine
        Coffee, Sanka, Postum, tea, or skimmed milk

SPECIAL NOTE: Try to learn to do without desserts. They are merely a bad habit going back to your childhood when a sweet was the reward for eating a big meal. You are no longer a child, and big meals will simply shorten your life.

If you absolutely "must," angel food cake, without any icing, is permitted.

SPECIAL NOTE: As soon as you can, get over the bad habit of bread. Bread is not the staff of life in our modern civilization. It is now denatured, with vitamins removed, and chiefly empty calories and dangerous starch.

This is your REDUCE AND STAY REDUCED diet pattern. These suggested foods can be combined in many ways to give variety to your menus. Many of your favorite recipes can be adapted to vegetable oil cookery.

Choose Freely

ALL FISH: The following are best-

Bluefish	Brook trout	Clams
Seabass	Pike	Crab meat
Flounder	Scallops	Oysters
Halibut	Sturgeon (fresh)	Lobster with vegetable
Haddock	Weakfish	oil sauce
Tuna fish (not canned)		Shrimps
Cod fish steaks		Mussels

FRUITS

Melon

Orange

Grapefruit

DO NOT EAT DRIED FRUITS

VEGETABLES AND LEGUMES

Eat as much as you wish—raw or cooked—with and even between meals.

Asparagus	Escarole
Beet greens	Peppers-green or red
Broccoli	Kale
Cabbage	Lettuce
Carrots	Mushrooms
Cauliflower	Mustard greens

Celery (but be careful of the large sodium content, and avoid if your physician tells you of any heart problem)

Chad	Mung bean sprouts
Collards	Parsley
Cucumbers	Radishes
Dandelion greens	Spinach
Endive	Summer squash
String beans	Watercress
Turnip greens	Onions

LOW CALORIC BEVERAGES:

Low caloric sodas

Coffee

Sanka

DESSERTS:

Learn to do without them as soon as possible. They represent a childhood habit, a reward for being good. You are no longer a child, and they can only shorten your life.

As a special treat—if you must—take angel food cake, without icing.

Orange, grapefruit, or melon are okay as a dessert.

Unsweetened gelatin (or made with a sugar substitute) is also okay.

SNACKS:

Cottage cheese, dry

Raw vegetables (see above list)

Hard boiled egg-whites (go good with cottage cheese)

Skimmed milk or fat-free buttermilk (made from skimmed milk)

Low caloric soft drinks

SUPPLEMENTS:

Brewers' yeast　　Wheat germ　　Bone meal

MEAT, CHEESE, POULTRY, AND EGGS:

Prepare according to cooking directions

Cut off all visible fat before eating

One serving is 3 oz. cooked weight

5 grams or less of fat per serving

Chicken breast (do not eat the skin!)

Heart

Liver—all kinds

Veal cutlet

Cottage cheese—½ cup (skimmed milk cottage cheese is best for you)

10 grams of fat (approx.) per serving

Beef—chipped, round, or shank

Tenderloin steak

Flank steak

Veal—all cuts

Kidney

Lamb—leg and loin chops

Chicken

Turkey

Cheese—one ounce

BUT—AVOID all cheese except cottage, pot, and farmer's cheese

15 grams of fat (approx.) per serving

Beef:

Chuck pot roast

Stew meat, lean

Hamburger, *lean only*

Tongue

T-bone steak

Porterhouse steak

RESTAURANT SUGGESTIONS FOR YOUR
REDUCE AND STAY REDUCED DIET

APPETIZER

Sea food cocktail

or

Orange, grapefruit, or melon

SOUP

Consommé   or   Bouillon

ENTREES: Broiled or baked without added fat.

Trim off all visible fat.

Chicken   Fish   Turkey   Beef tenderloin

Chicken or shrimp chow mein   Chicken chop suey

SALAD ENTREES

Shrimp   Lobster   Chicken

Tuna   Crab   Fruit

SALADS

Vegetable   Vinegar and oil dressing

Mixed green with tomato

PICKLES AND RELISHES

Avoid salted foods and relishes if you have a cardiac problem, a kidney disturbance, or if you are retaining fluid. *Follow your doctor's advice,* and do not try to treat yourself.

DESSERTS

Desserts are for children, as a sweet treat. The modern adult knows that desserts are dangerous and shorten life. *Learn to omit desserts* as a lesson in maturity, a lesson in self-control, and because you want better health and longer life.

IF YOU MUST—Angel food cake without icing

Orange, grapefruit, or melon

Gelatin with sugar-substitute flavoring

IMPORTANT . . .

1. It is best to avoid liquids one hour before, during, and for two hours after meals. Water retention is a problem in obesity.

2. Do NOT add salt to your food.

THE NEW CANTOR COCKTAIL FORMULA

The Cantor Cocktail may be prepared to taste exactly like a creamy-rich malted milkshake. You will require a one ounce measuring glass (a whiskey glass) and a blender of the Osterizer or Waring type.

The formula consists of two to three ounces of skimmed milk (preferably the vitamin-fortified skim milk now commercially available in all supermarkets), one ounce of safflower oil, and three ounces of your favorite low caloric soda.

Blend in the blender to form a frothy, creamy mixture. Note that all ingredients must be kept in the refrigerator.

A variation in the quantity of skimmed milk (two to three ounces) may be made for individual variation in taste and texture. A similar latitude of formula is permitted with the soda (two to four ounces).

My personal preference is for a "1-2-3" formula:

Safflower oil	1 ounce
Skimmed milk	2 ounces
Coffee-flavored, non-caloric soda	3 ounces

When this is homogenized in the blender, approximately eight ounces of a delicious, frothy, creamy mixture results.

GENERAL DIET RULES FOR BETTER HEALTH AND LONGER LIFE

1. Do not eat any food made from starch. Avoid sugar and sweets.
2. Do not eat high fat-content foods (whole milk, cream, butter, egg yolk, meat fat, ordinary margarine)
3. Eat fish as often as possible.
4. Lean meat, hard-cooked egg whites, cottage cheese, pot cheese, farmer's cheese, or poultry without the skin may be substituted for fish at some meals.
5. If you are not losing weight fast enough, you are either eating too much, or the wrong foods.
   Stay on your REDUCE AND STAY REDUCED diet.
6. The less you eat, the longer you will live.
7. Don't add salt to your food.
8. Keep water off the table. You will eliminate *water weight*.

9. Don't mistake thirst for hunger. If you feel you just must eat, try coffee, tea, clear bouillon, low caloric sodas, or Sucaryl-sweetened lemonade.

BUT—don't drink anything one hour before, DURING, or two hours after meals. Don't drink at bedtime.

10. If anxiety demands a food tranquilizer, try half a grapefruit or a slice of melon.

11. Let a salad be your first course—with safflower oil and lemon juice dressing. A big, bulky salad served first is healthful and fills the stomch.

THESE ARE YOUR *LUCKY ELEVEN* RULES FOR A SLIMMER FIGURE

The famous Cantor Cocktail

The Cantor Cocktail (so named by my patients) is highly nutritious. It provides polyunsaturated fats in the right amount. You must eat as little fat in your diet as possible, and most of it should be polyunsaturated. Polyunsaturated fats are liquid at room temperature, and the best ones are safflower oil, corn oil, and sunflower seed oil.

If you follow the principles of the Magic Diet and *drink the Cantor Cocktail* before each meal, you will be taking the right amount and type of fat. The unsaturated liquid fats in the Cantor Cocktail will then replace the hard, solid, excess fat in your body. You will develop softer, more rounded curves. You will lose weight. You will lose your dowager hump, girls, and become more youthful in contour.

The hard fat deposits in your arteries will go away, and your arteries will become more flexible. Since you are as old as your arteries, you will become *internally younger*. This will add years to your life.

Drinking the Cocktail before meals will reduce your appetite. The fat in the Cocktail satisfies the appetite and fills the stomach. You will want less food, and you will need less food. The Cocktail by itself offers sufficient food, and if supplemented by a multivitamin and mineral tablet or capsule, it can keep you healthy and prolong your life—*even if you eat nothing else.* So do not be disturbed by the fact that the famous Cocktail depresses your appetite. After all, that is exactly what you want!

DESIRABLE WEIGHTS FOR MEN
of ages 25 and over
Weight in Pounds According to Frame (In Indoor Clothing)

HEIGHT (with shoes on) 1-inch heels Feet Inches		SMALL FRAME	MEDIUM FRAME	LARGE FRAME
5	2	112–120	118–129	˙126–141
5	3	115–123	121–133	129–144
5	4	118–126	124–136	132–148
5	5	121–129	127–139	135–152
5	6	124–133	130–143	138–156
5	7	128–137	134–147	142–161
5	8	132–141	138–152	147–166
5	9	136–145	142–156	151–170
5	10	140–150	146–160	155–174
5	11	144–154	150–165	159–179
6	0	148–158	154–170	164–184
6	1	152–162	158–175	168–189
6	2	156–167	162–180	173–194
6	3	160–171	167–185	178–199
6	4	164–175	172–190	182–204

DESIRABLE WEIGHTS FOR WOMEN
of ages 25 and over

HEIGHT (with shoes on) 2-inch heels Feet Inches		SMALL FRAME	MEDIUM FRAME	LARGE FRAME
4	10	92– 98	96–107	104–119
4	11	94–101	98–110	106–122
5	0	96–104	101–113	109–125
5	1	99–107	104–116	112–128
5	2	102–110	107–119	115–131
5	3	105–113	110–122	118–134
5	4	108–116	113–126	121–138
5	5	111–119	116–130	125–142
5	6	114–123	120–135	129–146
5	7	118–127	124–139	133–150
5	8	122–131	128–143	137–154
5	9	126–135	132–147	141–158
5	10	130–140	136–151	145–163
5	11	134–144	140–155	149–168
6	0	138–148	144–159	153–173

For girls between 18 and 25, subtract 1 pound for each year under 25.

And so, we come to the realization that this gourmet diet, combined with the Cantor Cocktail, is a longevity diet. It is also an *automatic, anti-obesity diet.*

You are now on your way to a slim, lovely figure. You are on your way to a longer life and greater vitality. You are on your way to a more mature personality. Every day, in every way, you are becoming slimmer and slimmer, younger and younger, happier and happier, healthier and healthier.

Your weight goal

I am going to let you set your own weight goal according to the schedule on page 149.

Points to remember:

1. Excess fat—either external or internal (in your arteries)—will shorten your life.

2. Obesity leads to diabetes, high blood pressure, heart disease, strokes, arthritis, kidney trouble, postural deformities, unhappiness, and perhaps even cancer.

3. Obesity is a psychosomatic problem.

4. The lazy thyroid may be responsible in some cases.

5. Obesity and Immaturity are closely related.

6. When you lose weight by using the psychosomatic method, you also become more mature, happier, healthier, and younger.

7. The Magic Gourmet Diet offers three meals a day, between meal snacks, delicious food, and you need never be hungry.

8. The psychosomatic method is rapid, pleasant, and you can do it yourself without dangerous drugs.

Chapter 9

HOW THE ENDOCRINE GLANDS GUIDE YOUR LIFE

How to use chapter 9

1. Check this list and see if you have any of the following symptoms:

> You are jittery
> Over-emotional
> Excitable
> You are losing weight rapidly but eating well
> You are gaining weight but eating relatively little
> Your eyes protrude in a glassy stare
> Your appetite is poor
> Your appetite is enormous
> You tire easily
> You are easily depressed
> Life doesn't seem worth living
> Your monthly periods are not regular
> You perspire easily and have moist palms
> Your face flushes easily
> Your hands tremble
> You are always thirsty
>   always hungry } (this may be
>   always passing your water } diabetes)
> You feel weak, and get a lift from candy, coffee, etc.

2. If you do have any of these symptoms, read this chapter NOW.
3. Then, turn back to Chapter 4 and fill out the important Conflict Check Chart.

4. Now turn to Chapter 5 and begin the simple Guided Association home sessions to get rid of repressed worries—the roots of your psychosomatic health-wreckers.
5. Now begin the Muscle Relaxation and the Self-Suggestion methods to learn how to Switch off Your Brain.
6. Practice the KEY WORD magic for instant action in muscle relaxation, instant sleep, instant peace of mind, etc.

What are the endocrine glands?

The endocrine glands we will consider include the thyroid, the pancreas, and the pituitary. Others are the adrenals, and the sex glands (ovaries and testicles). These glands produce vital secretions that pour into your blood stream, secretions that control your body's metabolism and certain vital body functions. The tiny pinch of thyroid secretion, for example, is so important that if it is lacking in our blood stream we become physically and mentally like a vegetable. If there is the tiniest fraction too much, we become jittery, excitable, overemotional, lose weight rapidly, and show all kinds of overactivity of our general metabolism.

The thyroid gland is located at the base of the neck, and sometimes it enlarges and the eyes protrude in a glassy, feverish stare. This is called *exophthalmos* and a toxic goiter.

The pituitary gland is the master gland, located at the base of the brain. It regulates many body functions and works in close cooperation with the thyroid and all other endocrine glands to control growth, sex hormones, and many of the basic life activities. There is an emotionally-connected disorder of this gland called *anorexia nervosa,* associated with extreme loss of appetite and general wasting of the body. We will discuss this later from the psychosomatic viewpoint, only because lower degrees of appetite loss are very common psychosomatic problems.

The pancreas is a gland connected with the intestinal tract, and part of this important organ contains a tissue called the Islands of Langerhans. This tissue secretes insulin. A deficiency of insulin causes diabetes, and too much insulin has the opposite effect, lowering the blood sugar, sometimes to dangerous shock and coma levels. These effects are often associated with anxiety states, as well as with organic changes in the pancreas.

But before we can intelligently consider these glands and

their psychosomatic disturbances, we must understand a little about the autonomic nervous system, which is discussed below.

Your autonomic (involuntary) nervous system

All of our important body functions, our internal, vital, life functions, are controlled through the autonomic nervous system. Most of this control is involuntary and reflex. It is just as well for us that this is so, for if we had to think about breathing and keeping the heart beating every minute of the day or night, we would soon tire of this monitoring and die. And so, Nature has provided automatic regulators for breathing, the beating of the heart, the functions of our intestines, and these regulators work with and through the autonomic nervous system.

But there is a higher control center in our thinking brain level, the cortex. We will have more to say about this later on, but it is evident that some degree of self-regulation of our autonomic nerves is at least theoretically possible by means of controlled thinking. And vice versa, our thinking areas may be disturbed by autonomic nervous system disturbances. You have already seen how this happens in psychosomatic disturbances of the heart and the intestinal tract. Now you know the mechanism.

How this vital function regulator works

This automatic system regulates your endocrine glands and your blood vessels, as well as your heart and intestinal tract. Once again, we see the importance of the *unit concept* in thinking of any part of the body and its functions. Whatever happens at any point in our body influences all other parts, and this influence takes place through our blood, our endocrine glands, our central nervous system, and our autonomic nervous system.

All sensations from all parts of our body, all information from our skin, eyes, ears, nose, muscles, blood vessels, intestines, etc., reach our brain through the nervous system. Some pass through the central nervous system and some through the autonomic system. Some use both sets of nerves. It is very much like having two independent telephone companies, each servicing different body regions but connected through a central switchboard, our brain.

Regulation of endocrine glands function is partly carried out through these nervous systems, especially the autonomic nerves. It is also controlled to some extent by substances in our blood stream. And finally, these important glands respond to our feelings and thoughts. This feeling and thought stimulus and response is carried largely through our autonomic nervous system. This is the crux of our present discussion, the reason why you should be aware of the closely integrated functions of your brain levels (both thinking and feeling levels), and your endocrine glands—communications being largely through the autonomic nervous system.

Can you control these autonomic-endocrine functions?

This is an important question. We touched upon the answer when we learned that the autonomic nervous system is connected with the controllable central nervous system through the highest cortical levels of the master switchboard of the brain. Experiments show that when areas of the cortex are stimulated, various autonomic functions are affected. And since the feeling and emotion brain areas are intimately connected with the thinking levels, it is evident that our thoughts will influence our feelings, our feelings will affect our thoughts, and both will act upon our heart, lungs, endocrine glands and intestines, through the autonomic nervous system. This is an important observation. It means that our deeply repressed emotions, our childhood fears, our adult anxieties may act through this mechanism to derange endocrine gland function, or the behavior of our heart, our lungs, our intestines, our blood vessels, and all other parts of our body. We already know this, of course, from our previous chapters. But now we come upon the mechanism through which it all happens. Once we understand the mechanism, we can begin to think of how to block, prevent or control such disturbances. This is the way we prevent and rid ourselves of the psychosomatic health-wreckers.

Since there are connections within the thinking level of our brain, we can reach these otherwise uncontrollable, autonomic-endocrine disturbances by learning how to control and direct our thoughts. We have already learned something about these

methods in the self-suggestion technique and in the deep relaxation methods (Chapter 5).

And we can get rid of the deeply repressed emotional dynamite of our distant or more recent past—the dangerously explosive material in the feeling brain level—by using the Guided
Association method in conjunction with the Conflict Check Chart.
This combination of methods (*See* Chapters 4 and 5) gives us
some degree of control over our endocrine glands, our autonomic
nervous system, and its derangements.

We are now ready to look at the psychosomatic health-
wreckers that are connected with the thyroid, the pituitary, and
the pancreas.

A pituitary-like dysfunction can be helped

We will begin by looking in on a typical adolescent girl, 18
years old, in my consulting room. She came to see me because of
a nutrition problem, weight loss. She had been eating well, perhaps too much, for her family doctor had advised that she cut
down on food and lose some weight. She lost seven pounds, and
then the problem arose. She could not stop losing weight, and her
family was worried.

She herself was not particularly worried, for she had continued all her school and social activities and did not feel weak
or otherwise distressed.

Further questions showed that her menstrual periods had
stopped, aside from a slight discomfort and a very slight "stain-
ing" at the usual time. This did not worry her because her mother
had experienced the same irregularity when she was a girl.   -

Aside from the evidences of abnormal weight loss, the physical and laboratory examinations showed nothing unusual. She
was reassured and given a high caloric diet. No medications were
ordered.

Still, the weight loss continued. She had just stopped eating.
She paid no attention to her very anxious parents. Curiously, she
even concealed her food in her room until she could dispose of
it, in order to avoid eating. But this did not interfere with her
general sense of well-being or her activities. She was a member
of her cheerleading squad, and even her team-mates were worried
about her appearance.

Our major clue that the problem was primarily emotional was in the fact that this young lady felt fine and carried on a stiff physical activity schedule despite her continuing weight loss. We can only surmise that the pituitary disturbance in this case was activated or aggravated by emotional stress. In other words, we are saying that this youngster, and others like her, stop eating, lose weight and cease menstruating because of deep-seated emotional conflicts. It is an unconscious rebellion in most cases, emotional starvation causing physical starvation.

The Conflict Check Chart provided some of the answers. Her younger brother was "the brain" of the family, idolized by both her mother and her father. He could have anything he wanted, while she had a limited budget, especially for her clothes. Her weight loss served several unconscious purposes: attracting her parents' attention and concern, costing them money for medical care, and now requiring a whole new wardrobe for her much slimmer figure. This was not altogether unconscious, for she did conceal food in her room rather than eat it.

She really loved her younger brother, admired his "brain," and indulged him as much as their parents did. But the repressed resentment ran deep and caused this major change in her eating habits. Her body adapted to the demands of her subconscious mind by reducing pituitary activity and the interconnected ovary activity. This stopped her monthly flow. She considered this "normal" since her mother had had irregular periods at her age; and since the mind thought it was normal, the body accepted the idea and the fact.

In this interesting youngster we see the way the mind and body work as a unit to cause psychosomatic changes and symptoms. Guided Association helped greatly, as did Substitute Aggression sessions directed against her parents and her brother. She soon became aware of the inner mechanism, learned to laugh at the whole problem, and began to eat again. Her parents naturally cooperated and bought her a fine new wardrobe (especially after I pointed out that it was cheaper than continued medical care).

How to treat anorexia nervosa

The condition we have been describing is usually called *anorexia nervosa* (nervous loss of appetite). It usually occurs in adolescent girls, and the degree of appetite loss may be relatively small or great. These youngsters are usually repelled by sex and don't even masturbate very much, if at all. Sometimes they are perfectionists who have developed this personality trend after strict toilet training (see Chapter 2 for the "Childhood Scars"). Sometimes they were feeding problems. It is obviously essential to use the Conflict Check Chart and the autobiography to locate such problems. But these scars are even more rapidly found by gentle questioning of the youngsters' parents.

The first step is reassurance of the child and her parents, and the next step is to show the youngster that she is behaving just as if she were still an infant. This degree of immaturity is not called for, and she can control it if she wants to. She is told that there are better ways to face and solve her problems, whatever they may be. So she doesn't like sex! Let's find out why and do something about it in a sensible way, rather than by the self-destruction of not eating.

So she is rebelling against her mother! There are better ways to solve her mother problems than by self-destruction, by wasting away, and by giving up her femininity.

I have seen some *anorexia nervosa* problems in patients who went to extremes of under-eating while on an obesity diet. These were usually adolescent girls who were simply showing an underlying hostility toward their mother, or responding to their mother's hostility. These are psychosomatic problems that require careful management by all the methods of this book, as well as by management of the mother and her problems. Parent-child hostility is always a complex problem, and both antagonists must be treated at the same time.

The pattern to be followed in the treatment of nervous loss of appetite is the basic FOUR-STEP METHOD. These are the four steps:

1. You outline your life story and family history of disease and causes of death. You stress your fears, especially your health and death fears.

2. You fill out your Conflict Check Chart, locating times of worry, stress, injury, tears, grief, violence, and all other emotional disturbances from birth to the present moment.

3. You see your physician for examination, explanation, and reassurance. Follow his advice.

4. You then rid yourself of these worries and fears—both past and present—by practicing the methods of Chapter 5;

Self-Suggestion and Instant Relaxation

Guided Association

Substitute Aggression Release

Every one of the patients you will read about in this book has used this basic FOUR-STEP METHOD to rid himself of psychosomatic symptoms. It is the method you will use.

Your thyroid and your emotions

Emotional disturbances always accompany thyroid problems, either as cause or effect. We need not consider those emotional problems that result from an overactive thyroid. When the thyroid overactivity is slowed by medications or surgery, such emotional problems usually disappear. We are especially interested in those thyroid problems that are triggered by emotional disturbances, for they will respond best to our methods of psychotherapy.

However, these same methods of treatment will be useful in the toxic, overactive thyroid, both during and after medical or surgical treatment. These treatment methods of deep relaxation, Guided Association, and the others are basic and should be applied in all forms of disease in conjunction with other forms of medical or surgical therapy as ordered by your physician. Of course, if the emotional disturbances are the result of a toxic thyroid, the medical or surgical treatment comes first, and the psychotherapy is supportive.

It is also important to realize that a state of basic, autonomic imbalance and emotional shock is often followed by a toxic thyroid condition. How can you tell whether or not your own autonomic nervous system is unbalanced? In most cases you will not be able to tell, and even your physician will find it difficult to know. But you can suspect an unstable autonomic nervous system if you sweat excessively, and especially if the palms of your hands are wet whenever you are emotionally disturbed.

Anxiety symptoms and early overactivity of the thyroid gland are so alike that even your physician will sometimes find it difficult to tell one from the other. It is important to know this so that you will not try to treat yourself, and also so that you will understand how stress may be followed by an overactive, toxic thyroid problem.

There are certain characteristic anxiety reactions in such cases. The sweating palms is one, and a flushing of the neck and lower face is another. A slight tremor of the fingertips, when the hands are extended, may be still another evidence of early thyroid overactivity, perhaps due to emotional stress.

Many of these patients tell of a sudden, severe emotional conflict just before their thyroid symptoms began. But every one of these sufferers must be given the benefit of release from repressed emotional problems of their entire lifetime, the type of release that is provided by the Check Chart, Guided Association, and the other methods of this book.

How Avis R. developed and overcame her anxiety thyroid problem

Avis R. was 33, married, with two children, a boy of 15, and a girl of 6. She had married while still in high school, despite her parents' protests and her youth, and in spite of the fact that her husband was 12 years older than she. Her marriage was a rebellion against her parents, for "I could not stand their constant bickering, their fighting over money, and I decided to marry someone who could support me right from the word go."

Her husband did support her, but he was not what she had expected sexually. "He comes home at night, plops in front of the television set, drinks beer, and falls asleep. Not exactly my idea of what marriage should be like." Worse still, she confessed that she had never had an orgasm. I told her that this was not uncommon, in spite of having children, and that we would need to re-educate her husband in sex matters if we were to correct this. At this she threw up her hands in despair and said that that would be impossible. He considered himself a great lover, and she had been "smart enough" to let him think so.

She had been very nervous for a long time and thought that she was on the verge of a nervous breakdown several times. This was at its worst right after her mother died, three years after her marriage. She felt "responsible," and thought that her marriage might have "broken her heart."

Examination showed the wet palms, the neck and lower face flush, and the finger tremor. The simple blood protein-bound iodine test indicated mild thyroid overactivity.

Avis responded well to explanation and reassurance. She was a very intelligent young lady, and had readily demonstrated both her independence and her willingness to compromise with life when she left her family, chose an older man, and then gave him a feeling of competence and manhood in his sex activity. She continued to cooperate in treatment, and the Conflict Check Chart and Guided Association revealed and released many specific emotional traumas of her past. Each time this occurred, she became much calmer, and the evidences of thyroid overactivity totally disappeared. Even her thyroid function tests showed a completely normal gland.

One more word of caution: Some thyroid anxiety problems require treatment with radioactive iodine or a partial removal of the thyroid to quiet the toxicity of the gland. In such cases the psychotherapy is of fundamental importance and must be started and continued right through such medical or surgical treatment. But it must be a combined treatment, and that is why you must always consult your physician if you suspect thyroid overactivity.

The lazy thyroid

We have already had something to say about thyroid underactivity in Chapter 8. The lazy thyroid is very common and is usually overlooked. Anyone who is overweight should be given the benefit of the doubt, even if there is very evident anxiety at the root of the overeating. There may also be a lazy thyroid in the background, causing the fat to pile up all over your body.

If you are overweight, see your physician for the protein-bound iodine test. This is a very simple test requiring only a small blood sample from an arm vein. It is very accurate and very quickly reported by a competent laboratory. It is more reliable than the breathing basal-metabolism test or the Achilles-heel reflex test.

If you have a lazy thyroid, in addition to correcting the emotional problems that usually accompany or underlie obesity, your physician will give you tiny, thyroid substance tablets to correct the deficiency. Your excess fat will melt away, and a proper diet will then help to keep you thin and lovely.

Joan had a lazy thyroid, was 31 pounds overweight, and was chronically unhappy. She was always tired, and preferred lying down to sitting or standing, and sleeping to being awake. In other words, she was in constant retreat from life. She was only 18, an early age for so complete a retreat.

She had been to several doctors, each of whom put her on a strict diet. She sometimes followed their instructions, and sometimes ignored them. In no case did she ever lose more than two or three pounds before she gave up trying. "I really don't eat so much," she complained, "but nobody believes me."

I believed her, and it was true. Her problem was the lazy thyroid, and the tiny, thyroid analog pills started her on a "miracle" of weight loss.

Her retreat from reality, however, was not entirely due to the lazy thyroid. She had many emotional problems at home and at school, and these required the Conflict Check Chart and Guided Association therapy to control. She became very efficient with Guided Association and used it daily at home. This is the best way to use this treatment, by yourself, in the privacy of your own home.

Low blood sugar and your health

Anxiety, sudden emotional distress, injury, fear, or even the threat of injury or stress—all may cause a rise in our blood sugar level. In a sense, this is a normal mechanism to help us adjust to the energy needs required for "fight or flight." Our body mobilizes sugar when it requires quick energy, since this is the most easily metabolized energy-producing substance. It is this ancient "fight or flight" mechanism that has helped man escape or overcome his enemies since the beginning of time.

This same mechanism is active during "normal" stress, such as war-time commands to charge the enemy, football and baseball competition, and even during examinations in school. In all such causes there may be an elevation of our blood sugar and the spilling over of some of this sugar into the urine. This stress response is not diabetes. Nor does it require treatment in most cases.

Little Arnold's mother came to me with her twelve year old son, both very agitated. Their family doctor had given them the bad news that Arnold had diabetes. The doctor had been very careful and had done both blood sugar and urine sugar studies. He had found sugar in the urine and a high level of blood sugar. They came to me because I had "cured" a neighbor of diabetes.

I told them that their neighbor had not had the usual type of diabetes, and that I had no such "cure." However, I repeated the tests and found them to be normal. The answer was that the tests had been made originally right after a difficult examination at school, an examination that had meant a great deal to the child. He feared that he had failed (He did not!).

I explained that an emotional rise in blood sugar, with some spillage into the urine, was not unusual. The youngster certainly did not have diabetes, and sugar tolerance tests showed that this was true. I suppose that this will go down in their neighborhood as another "cure" of diabetes.

Incidentally, the neighbor who had been "cured" of diabetes actually did have diabetes, but it basically was of emotional stress origin, and the treatment was simply Guided Association and relaxation training combined with an appropriate diet. Her diabetes had been under this control for over 12 years.

Is diabetes a stress disease?

Diabetes may obviously be precipitated by stress. But there is probably an inherited deficiency in the Islands of Langerhans, the part of the pancreas that produces insulin. It is probable that in the absence of this genetic deficiency, stress will not cause diabetes. So you must consider your own family history and see if there is diabetes in your background. Of course, you may have diabetes as the first in your family. On the other hand, we know that stress of all kinds acts through our autonomic nervous system and our hypothalamus (the emotion-feeling level of our brain) to raise our blood sugar. If there is any predisposition to diabetes, conscious or unconscious emotional disturbances (and perhaps especially those which are repressed at the hypothalamic Silent Level) may trigger diabetic trouble.

The famed Menninger of the Menninger Clinic once reported on 30 cases of mental disorder in diabetics. The interesting point is that as their mental condition improved their diabetes also got better, *without insulin and without dietary treatment!* These patients all had unconscious, emotional disturbances, and all were considered to be quite disturbed emotionally prior to the development of their diabetes. With appropriate psychotherapy, blood sugar levels returned to normal, and these patients all developed a normal ability to utilize sugar. These are anxious, depressed, neurotic people, all of whom were made worse with each emotional crisis.

As is the case with all the psychosomatic health-wreckers, repressed emotional conflicts were at the root of the trouble. An acute emotional crisis may precipitate the problem and bring it to the physician's attention, but the real trouble goes very deep.

To root out such repressed emotional dynamite requires careful study, the Conflict Check Chart, and Guided Association therapy.

The basic FOUR-STEP METHOD again comes into play. But since these are especially anxious, depressed, nervous patients, they must pay special attention to these self-affirmation and relaxation methods. Instant peace of mind is their goal. If diabetes is your problem, practice the Chapter 5 methods for Instant Relaxation and Instant Sleep. They will help to insulate you against the daily annoyances and stress of living.

Do this all through your Guided Association sessions, putting yourself into a state of complete relaxation from the neck down while reliving the emotional distress of your past. Naturally you cannot do this when you use the Substitute Aggression method, but you will feel much relaxed after ridding yourself of repressed aggression, and you will then be able to go into a deep state of Instant Relaxation.

The patient I will now tell you about below used this Four Step Method with great success in an emotionally-triggered case of diabetes. You can do the same, with the same pattern of treatment.

Phil was an artistic young man of 34, an interior decorator who really knew and enjoyed his work. His male-female hormone balance seemed to lean in the female direction, judging from his mannerisms, dress, and the fact that he had no interest in the opposite sex. He was very much attached to his mother and lived at home. His father was dead, but he openly said that he had hated "the man," and that his father had been "beastly to mother."

He complained of chronic fatigue, and felt that "life was just getting to be too much." He did not think that either his employer or his clients really appreciated the "blood and sweat" that went into his work. "I'm not complaining," he said, "but I'd just as soon wake up dead." This was obviously a much depressed man.

His blood sugar was elevated, and he spilled sugar into his urine. The diagnosis was diabetes, probably on an emotionally-triggered basis. There was no family history of this disease.

He was placed on an appropriate diet and started on psychotherapy with Guided Association. Naturally, we also discussed the question of the value of life, and we came to the conclusion that it had value at least in the sense that there was nothing better that either of us had to offer! We decided that he would continue to give it a try on that basis, at least until his diabetes improved. It was my opinion, as I told him, that much of his depression might be due to the diabetes itself. If so, he might feel better inclined toward life if his health were improved. He agreed, and he went at the treatment with a will.

His improvement was rapid, both in his diabetes and in his sense of well-being. His blood sugar rapidly returned to normal, he spilled no more sugar in his urine, and he decided to stay alive. Indeed, he went into business on his own, and has been very successful.

Low blood sugar and your psychosomatic health

It often happens that our blood sugar falls below the normal level, leaving us weak and easily fatigued. This is sometimes called *functional hyperinsulinism,* a condition in which the body seems to produce too much insulin. Such swings of sugar level may also occur from the abuse of the coffee habit. But they are usually associated with anxiety. We must be careful, in all cases, to be certain that there is no tumor of the pancreas throwing off the excess insulin and causing exactly the same symptoms. When this has been ruled out by your physician, the low blood sugar may be considered to be the result of an anxiety state. Worry does it!

Mary, a 23-year-old secretary, had such a condition. She always carried candy with her, for she had found that a candy bar quickly snapped her out of her feeling of weakness and worry. A glass of orange juice did the same, but this was not always available when she needed it most.

Mary was unhappy with her work, her boss, and her home life. She was continuously anxious about not being married. We could do little about these things directly, but she was helped by *reassurance* that her condition was not serious. She was also much improved by Guided Association treatments, most of which she carried out in her own home. With lessening anxiety, with acceptance of conditions she could not change, and with the change of conditions under her control, she improved to the point that her "attacks" were reduced to very infrequent intervals, all easily traced to current emotional stress. Her general irritability and frustration tolerance had much improved, and things that had formerly "set her off" into a state of weakness, distress, fear of death, confusion and sometimes exhaustion no longer bothered her.

Stress and how we adapt to it

Hans Selye, famed Montreal researcher, has taught us that we all react to stress in pretty much the same way, and he describes this reaction as a "general adaptation syndrome." In these terms, when the adaptation fails, we would develop psychosomatic health problems—diseases of adaptation. Selye pointed out that our exposure to stress causes toxic substances to be released into our bodies, and we respond to this by such conditions as a rapid pulse and heart rate, peptic ulcer, fluid retention, elevated blood sugar followed by a fall in the sugar level, and by other body changes.

These toxic substances then stimulate the pituitary gland to discharge certain hormones which act on our adrenal glands. Our adrenal glands then produce special hormones to increase and improve our resistance. This helps to reverse the changes already described and keeps us alive. But if the stress continues—whether it be emotional or physical in an external sense—we get worse and may die.

The cause of death? High blood pressure, hardening of the

kidney arteries, heart failure or coronary thrombosis, arthritis in its worse forms, in brief, a failure to adapt to the stress, the failure striking and damaging the entire body-mind unit.

Does this sound like psychosomatic disease? It is, all the way through, for the stress of emotional disturbances, whether of recent or childhood vintage, acts in just this way. It acts through the hypothalamus, the autonomic nervous system, the pituitary and the adrenals, to damage all parts of our body. The result? The psychosomatic health-wreckers.

In summary . . .

We have now seen (1) how our endocrine glands act to determine our health and our deviations from normal health patterns. (2) We have learned the relationship of our endocrine glands to our autonomic nervous system. (3) We have found out how this nervous system is closely interconnected with the feeling level of our brain and how this feeling level communicates with our brain's thinking level.

And we now know, (4) that emotional disturbances of the past and present, and, particularly, repressed emotions, may trigger serious body disease, acting through these very mechanisms. (5) This disease may take the form of high or low blood sugar, thyroid under- or overactivity, pituitary or adrenal gland disturbances, and it may even kill us. This is the mechanism of your psychosomatic health-wreckers. This is *how* they undermine our health and may even take our lives.

Points to remember:

1. Your endocrine glands—thyroid, pituitary, pancreas, adrenals, and others—all work together to keep your body functioning normally.
2. Stress of all kinds, especially repressed emotional problems of our recent or childhood past, may be at the root of the endocrine gland disturbances.
3. Thyroid health-wreckers may take the form of overactivity or underactivity of this gland.
4. Pancreatic health-wreckers may be in terms of overactivity or underactivity of insulin formation, causing a low blood sugar or its opposite, diabetes.

5. Pituitary health-wreckers may be related to marked loss of appetite and body wasting,
   or to general pituitary-adrenal gland disturbances, leading to high blood pressure, heart disease, coronary artery disease, general arterial changes, kidney disease, arthritis, general loss of body resistance, and death.
6. These endocrine-hypothalamus, autonomic nervous system disturbances have been explained, and you now know that they can often be helped by the methods described in this book.

Chapter 10

HOW TO CONTROL BONE, JOINT, AND BACK PAINS

How to use chapter 10

1. Check this list and see if you have any of the following symptoms:

Backache
Muscle spasm
Joint pain
Joint stiffness
Muscle pain
Stiff muscles
Swollen joints,
 with or without fever or general weakness
General aches and pains
Neuritis pains
Tense or tight muscles
Poor range of motion in any joint or limb
Back stiffness

2. If you do have any of these symptoms, read this chapter NOW.
3. Then, turn back to Chapter 4 and fill out the Conflict Check Chart. This will tell you *why* you have these troubles (in addition to any injury you may have sustained). This is very important, and must be done before going on to the next step.
4. Now, turn back to Chapter 5 and begin the simple Guided Association sessions to get rid of your worries and fears. Worry and fear are the main roots of psychosomatic health-wreckers.
5. Now, begin the all-important Muscle Relaxation and the Self-

Suggestion methods to learn how to relax stiff joints and muscles, and how to switch off pain.

6. Practice the KEY WORD magic for instant action in muscle relaxation, instant pain release, and instant sleep.

Bone, joint, and back pains are of tremendous importance to each of us, for we will suffer with one or more of such pains if we live long enough. Arthritis is one of the most disabling diseases. It is perhaps the oldest known chronic disease. It is one of the most serious and one of the most frequent chronic cripplers today. Worst of all, we do not know of any specific cause, and we have no specific treatment. There have been many fads and fancies in the treatment of this terrible disorder, and many quacks have become rich deceiving these sufferers. In my opinion and experience, many of these arthritis patients are suffering from a basic emotional disturbance acting through the autonomic nervous system. This probably works to produce the arthritic changes by aggravating other factors such as infection, injury, general body wear and tear, and other disorders. We will have much more to say about this later on.

Back pain is one of the serious problems faced by industry as well as by the general population. It is difficult to pin down the nature, the origin, or the best management of this problem. The loss of time from work, the many claims against compensation carriers, and the chronic disability that results make back pain an important problem.

Muscle pain is also very common and is basically due to emotional reactions to stress, acting through tense, unrelaxing muscles. This factor, by the way, is important in all bone, joint, muscle, and back disturbances. We will have much to say about this, and you are already well informed in the management of the tense, spastic, unrelaxed muscle.

Rheumatism and what it really means

The word *rheumatism* has been much abused and misused by both the physician and the layman. It is a kind of wastebasket diagnosis, very much like "grippe." It doesn't mean very much unless you take it to include all types of aches and pains in muscles, joints, and other parts of the musculo-skeletal system, including arthritis.

We used to think that rheumatism was a disease due to localized infection, and we advised removal of this "focal infection." God alone knows how many tonsils and adenoids, how many normal appendixes, gall bladders and other organs lie on the altar of focal infection. This was commonly accepted medical practice, and not quack therapy.

I still think that the patient with any of the conditions that belong under the general term "rheumatism" should be kept in the best possible general health. But this is not accomplished by indiscriminate removal of "diseased" organs. When an organ or tissue is obviously diseased, however, it should be properly treated or removed, not as specific therapy for the arthritis or other form of "rheumatism," but to put the patient in better health, a better state of general metabolism to fight the "rheumatism."

Don't surrender to arthritis

It is easy enough to throw up your hands in despair when you hear that there is no specific treatment for arthritis, no new wonder drug, no magic. There are regularly occurring fads, claims for miracles; and arthritic sufferers flock to the new miracle worker or to the pharmacy. But these invariably prove disappointing, frustrating, or worse. The vogue has a mildly beneficial effect based upon the patient's expectation and hope and faith, and then the condition goes back to its original severity—sometimes even worse.

But something can be done about this psychosomatic health-wrecker. A great deal can be done by you, by your family physician, and most of all, by what you have already learned in this book. After all, there are emotional undercurrents in this condition, as in all others, and you can do something to release your repressed emotional dynamite. You can also practice the muscle-relaxing training you now know and release your arthritic joints from the muscle strain and spasm that makes for most of your present lack of motion. In some cases, there may even be an improvement in the joints themselves, changes visible on X-rays.

A word of warning—don't waste your money or your time on irregular practitioners or on quacks. Don't get caught up in the latest fads. Stick to the diet, medications, physiotherapy, or other measures recommended by your family doctor. Aspirin is probably just as effective as any other medicine and is not at all expensive.

Your family physician may recommend one or two tablets every four hours. Do as he suggests. Then, follow the methods we will now outline.

Your life patterns and arthritis

It would seem that the patterns of stress in arthritis are very much the same as those in all other psychosomatic disturbances, such as ulcerative colitis, asthma, and the like. There is always chronic or acute environmental stress from lack of work or money, family worries, grief, violence, or perhaps hostility within the family itself.

These patients have great difficulty in adjusting to life, not only because of the chronic disability of the arthritis, but also because of the underlying, repressed emotional disturbances. It is a vicious circle, a cat chasing its own tail, and we can't tell which comes first in this emotion-disability-emotion cycle. In any case, we must locate and get rid of all repressed emotional dynamite, and this calls for the Conflict Check Chart and Guided Association sessions.

Self-suggestion treatment

As you release these emotional tensions, and as you get rid of repressed aggression at the unconscious Silent Level by reactivating and reliving the disturbing episodes of your past, you may find that your spastic muscles and motion-limited joints will relax and move more freely. You must concentrate at the same time on the self-suggestion procedures, directing your suggestions to *better and better muscle and joint action every day in every way.*

You must also engage in daily sessions of muscle relaxation training. Your muscles have become quite spastic, tight and difficult to relax as a result of your joint problems. The tight, unrelaxed muscles have, in turn, further limited your joint motion. You must break this vicious cycle by practicing muscle relaxation as often as possible. As your muscles relax, you must very gradually increase the range of motion of your involved joints. You must also very gradually increase the use of those joints by daily walking. As you walk, and in rhythm with each step, practice the self-suggestion affirmation: *Every day, in every way, my muscles and joints are becoming better and better, stronger and stronger, healthier and healthier.* Or you may simply say to yourself, in rhythm with your walking: *Better and better, better and better.*

Use such self-suggestion affirmations at every possible opportunity, while eating, working, resting, walking, and before going to sleep. The before-sleep time is naturally one of the very best for such therapy, as you know.

How this has worked for others

The proof of the pudding is always in the eating, and you must find out for yourself. One of the most skeptical patients I ever treated was a movie and stage actor who was beginning to show the early evidences of arthritic joints. His fingers and shoulders were major problem areas, and the stiffness and pains were accompanied by a general fatigue, a "sense of weariness," and a gradually increasing depression.

He had been examined by topflight physicians on both coasts, and the diagnosis was rheumatoid arthritis. It had begun acutely with swelling of the finger joints, some fever, and general weakness and disability. He now pictured himself sitting in a wheel chair, "crippled and useless." As he said this, I could see him living this scene in his mind, feeling it in his bones. I asked him who had told him that he would be so crippled. One of the doctors had answered his question on the possible course of the disease by telling him that chronic disability and crippling is often the outcome, although it might take many years. But the fear resulted from the fact that this was exactly what had happened to his father.

I told him of the possible role of the emotions in such conditions, and he seemed to understand and accept the mechanism as described. We then went over the Conflict Check Chart and the Guided Association procedures, and he went away with both, not entirely convinced but willing to try. He did very well with the Chart and was very honest and searching in his self-evaluation.

His home life had been very disturbing to him from childhood on through adolescence. He had two brothers, both older, who dominated and tormented him, giving him a serious inferiority complex. He was convinced that he never would amount to much, accepting his brothers' evaluation of himself. He wished his brothers would die, and he often plotted how to kill them. When he was twelve, one of his brothers developed a virus pneumonia and very nearly did die. This gave my patient a terrible sense of guilt, and he felt responsible for his brother's illness and near-death. He realized that he had been "playing the role of God," as he looked back upon it now, thinking himself the cause of his brother's illness. His evaluation during Guided Association was that his arthritis could have been his own self-punishment for wishing his brother dead.

Another major problem throughout his entire lifetime was his abnormal attachment to his mother and his open hatred for his father. His mother took his side in all quarrels with his brother, but his father was very severe with him and often "used his belt" to punish his childish pranks. In adult life he had "little use" for women, "except as window dressing," and his three marriages were marriages "in name only."

When he re-enacted the past emotional traumas in present tense, it was a very dramatic and stirring experience. I regretted his departure for the West Coast, but he continued by self-managed Guided Association during the months he was away. His reports were very encouraging.

To this point, seven years after beginning treatment, he has been free from further episodes of arthritic pain or joint change. It was not a straight-line improvement, but steady and very effective. He also told me that he felt he had become a better actor and a better person as a result of the Guided Association release of repressed emotional problems of his childhood.

Specific emotional factors in arthritis

One excellent study in this difficult field showed that "environmental stress, especially poverty, grief, and family worry, seem to bear more than a chance relationship to the onset and exacerbations of rheumatoid arthritis." Rheumatoid arthritis is sometimes called chronic infectious arthritis and is the type described in the actor's case history. *Osteoarthritis* is the other major type. Regardless of type, both forms are always associated with emotional problems, either in the beginning or afterward.

The problem of earning a living, the difficulties within the patient's own family, the fear and despondency associated with this chronic disease—all combine to form a tremendous stress burden.

But the probability is that the emotions are merely one factor in the cause and aggravation of this disease, as they are in all disease. They will play the triggering role in some patients. In others, they will be the long-standing mechanism that finally allows infection or some other factor to break into the body defense in the region of the bones and joints. The bones and joints may be especially vulnerable owing to previous injury or, perhaps, because of an inherited weakness.

These arthritis patients are often poorly adjusted in their sexual development and relations. Women may be tomboys in early life and masculine in their marriage role. However, these personality patterns and traits are not found exclusively in arthritis patients, and we must admit that there are no specific emotional patterns in these cases.

Whatever the emotional disturbance, it must be revealed by the Conflict Check Chart, and released by Guided Association treatment. Reassurance is most important since these patients are always very worried about being completely crippled by the disease.

What about osteoarthritis?

There is little to add to the usual idea that this form of arthritis is the result of old age and injury. But I have seen cases that responded well to the uncovering and release of emotional distress, repressed in the unconscious mind. There is an overgrowth of bone in the joints, and your physician will make the diagnosis on examination and X-ray. Don't give up hope. I have seen such bone changes improve, the arthritic pain lessening, and the bone over-growth stopping as the emotional stresses were relieved.

Alice was such a problem, and she was crippled by fear and despondency almost as much as by her disease. She had given up all hope of ever being free from pain. And she had reconciled herself to life in a wheel chair.

Alice had lost her husband in an automobile crash, while she was driving. She had injured her knee and one shoulder and had suffered severe concussion, with short-term loss of consciousness. She had never forgiven herself, although the fault was not hers. The other driver was drunk, an adolescent who had no right driving in his condition. But Alice assumed all the blame, and her arthritis was triggered by her grief and guilt.

As she responded to Guided Association reliving of this emotionally painful incident, she gradually began to see the accident in its proper perspective, and her final release from self-recrimination was quite rapid, almost dramatic. As she improved emotionally, the limiting muscle spasm and pain also lessened and finally became relatively insignificant. She returned to normal living and ultimately remarried.

Aches and pains without arthritis

We all have aches or pains in our muscles or joints at one time or another. Usually they do not last long and may even be associated with changes in the weather. There may be some muscle or even joint motion stiffness in such cases. But there is no arthritis, and the diagnosis is usually *myositis* (muscle inflammation), or *fibrositis* (another "wastebasket" diagnosis, meaning, "inflammation in the fibrous connective tissue").

Frankly, I wonder if there is such a disease as myositis, unless it is connected with a definite injury to a muscle. And I do not believe in fibrositis any more than I would accept most of the grippe diagnoses. But, regardless of label, there are aches and pains in the muscls and joints that cannot be accounted for in the general arthritis types. If you are a sufferer from such aches and pains, it is most important to be reassured right now that you do not have arthritis or any other crippling disease. You will get better and there will be no disability. You can help yourself get better faster if you will concentrate on the muscle relaxing training (*See* Chapter 5). And you should also use the self-healing, positive affirmations you have already learned in this book.

One of my most troubled patients had such aches and pains in her legs and arms and was also distressed by lower back pain. At times, she complained of headache and also ran an occasional slight fever. The examinations never showed any evidence of arthritis or any other muscle, bone, or joint disease. Her mother suffered from severe, disabling, arthritis of the type that develops with aging. One of her two older brothers had early evidence of rheumatoid arthritis (the infectious type). This was enough to frighten her into a constant anxiety state. Every little bone, muscle, or joint ache or pain was magnified by fear, until she was fully convinced that she was on the way to full disability. "I can see myself in a wheel chair," was her most frequent moan. She limited her activities whenever she felt these aches or pains, and soon would have truly been crippled by the self-induced wasting of inactive muscles.

I explained this to her, showing her how she was herself causing the very problem she feared—restriction of joint motion. I showed her how to relax during one of her "attacks," and she was amazed how quickly the pain and spasm disappeared. I pointed out that she herself had corrected the condition, just as she herself had caused it. I gave her a name for her "disease"—*anxiety spasm*. I told her to use this name whenever she felt the pains and aches and then to proceed as shown, to get rid of the spasm resulting from her anxiety.

We used Guided Association as well as explanation and reassurance, to release her unspoken fears. She did very well, and now has few complaints.

The emotional patterns of "aches and pains" problems

The "aches and pains" patients are anxious, tense, fearful, and worried about the past to the point of actually living in the past more than in the present. They never seem to be enjoying themselves. The future is a source of worry to the point of despondency. I usually tell them that none of us will ever get out of this world alive. They accept this gravely, and without a smile. They have little humor and get little pleasure from life. They cannot relax and often cannot sleep well.

Some of them identify themselves with relatives or even neighbors with serious, crippling arthritis. They often have a chronic backache that prevents them from carrying on normal work or household duties.

If you are an "aches and pain" patient, stop now and take a good long, honest look at yourself. Now go to your family doctor, if you have not already been there a "million times," and ask him if you have arthritis or any serious crippling disease. If you have, let him prescribe for you. If you do not, let me prescribe for you as follows:

Start to practice my relaxation methods every day, as long as possible each day, until you can relax yourself instantly with the

Key Words. Learn to relax so quickly and easily that you can fall asleep almost as soon as you lie down. But spend a few moments each night, just before falling asleep, with the positive self-affirmations. Tell yourself: *Every day, in every way, I am becoming stronger and stronger, healthier and healthier, happier and happier, younger and younger.*

Use such affirmations during the day as you practice your deep relaxation. This is very important, and you may use whatever words you wish to affirm your improving health and happiness.

Your next step is to get rid of smouldering, repressed emotional tensions. You will do this with the Conflict Check Chart and the Guided Association method (Chapters 4 and 5). You will be pleased to find that as you uncover and release these stress situations, the pains and aches will gradually disappear. One day, you will probably wake up to find that you are well.

But this is still not enough. Now you must begin to live each day, one day at a time. You can't possibly do more. In fact, no one can live more than one heartbeat at a time. Don't set yourself into the dead concrete of the past and don't live in constant fear of the future. You have no lease on life, no guarantee that you have a future, any more than I do. So make the most of today. Learn to enjoy life NOW. Let that be your key word for living each day—NOW. Smile, relax, and have fun. Tomorrow may be too late. Enough sorrow, aches, and pains. Smile every time you say this word and try to have fun NOW.

How to overcome back problems

As you now know, perhaps from your own sad experience, low back pain is a very common cause of chronic disability. Perhaps you have lost time from your work because of this painful condition.

Our back is a weak link and has been ever since man began to walk upright. This is especially so if we are carrying around many pounds of excess weight, or if we are wearing high heels. An old joke has it that woman is a constipated animal with high heels and a pain in the back. It is no joke if you are the one with the pain in the back.

You may have some bone, joint, nerve, muscle, or other orthopedic problem, and if you do, you should have it diagnosed and treated by a specialist in this field. But if your X-rays and other studies show no disease, begin the treatment methods just outlined for you. You may be suffering from an emotionally-triggered or aggravated back muscle spasm. You may be trying to escape your responsibilities to yourself or your family. You may be trying to escape daily problems, stresses, and strains that we all have to live with and endure. Or you may be trying to escape repressed emotional problems of your past, problems that can only be brought to the surface by the Conflict Check Chart and Guided Association.

Even if your condition requires medical management, you can help yourself to get well faster if you learn the relaxation methods. Ask your doctor, and he will tell you that much of your pain is due to muscle spasm. If you can control or eliminate that spasm, you can help yourself enormously. The rest is up to you.

Points to remember:

1. Arthritis is the oldest known chronic disease.
2. There is no specific treatment for arthritis, so stay away from anyone who promises you a cure, a secret remedy, a magic charm.
3. There are probably many causes acting together to produce arthritis, including low resistance, injury to the joint or joints, fear, general anxiety, past or present emotional problems.
4. Release from the emotional tensions is often associated with some improvement. But you must also be under the care of your physician.
5. Relaxation of tense muscles will often relieve much of the associated pain. You can release such tension yourself.
6. You can also free yourself from the emotional pain and spasm of past disturbances by using the Conflict Check Chart and Guided Association.
7. Rheumatism is a wastebasket diagnosis. So is myositis and fibrositis, unless caused by a definite injury.
8. General aches and pains and low back problems will often respond to reassurance and relaxation therapy.
9. You must also learn to live in the present, making NOW your Key Word.

Chapter II

HOW TO OVERCOME SKIN DISORDERS

How to use chapter 11

1. Check this list and see if you have any of the following symptoms:

   Acne
   Inflamed skin
   Skin irritation
   Itch
   Hives
   Pimples
   Rectal itch
   Vaginal itch
   Nervous skin rash
   Eczema
   Blisters
   Fever sores
   Sensitivity to cosmetics, drugs, chemicals, etc.
   Scaly skin
   Nervous dermatitis (inflamed skin due to "nerves")

2. If you do have any of these symptoms, read this chapter NOW.
3. Then, turn back to Chapter 4 and fill out the Conflict Check Chart. This tells you *why* you have these psychosomatic skin wreckers.
4. Now, turn to Chapter 5 and begin the simple Guided Association sessions to get rid of your worries and fears. These are at the root of your skin problem.

5. Now, begin the important Muscle Relaxation and the Self-Suggestion methods to learn how to relax all parts of your body, how to Switch Off Itch and Irritation, etc.
6. Practice KEY WORD magic for Instant Action in muscle relaxation, instant pain release, instant itch control, and instant sleep.

Multiple causation

There is no single cause for any disease. This may seem to be a curious statement, and it requires an explanation. What I am about to say applies to all disease, all psychosomatic disorders, and not just to skin disease.

At the present time, medical thinking is biased toward bacteria, viruses, and parasites as *the* cause of disease. The part that bacteria, viruses, and parasites play in disease is well established— so well-founded that we sometimes forget that there must be other factors at work to prepare the way for the bacteria, viruses, and parasites. Who will deny that the typhoid bacillus "causes" typhoid fever, and the tubercle bacillus "causes" tuberculosis? But this is only *part* of the truth.

When we speak of bacteria as *the* cause of disease, we are seeing only one tree in a forest. This is like the viewers of a painting, the artist seeing the brush strokes and technical details, the interior decorator seeing only the way the picture would fit into a particular room, the dealer seeing only dollars, and the buyer seeing perhaps a good investment. The physician is aware of such abstraction of one or two points from a total picture, and is becoming even more aware as he learns more about psychosomatic medicine. He knows that bacteria alone are not enough, and that emotional disturbances, general stress, resistance of local tissues and the general body resistance, heredity, specific sensitivity or allergy, climate and other environmental factors, available food, and many other things are part of the multiple causation in any disease. We must understand this clearly if we are to really understand psychosomatic disorders and not go off half-cocked in our thinking.

How does this fit the skin disease picture?

Skin disease is also subject to the multiple causation rule. Just as it takes a low resistance, perhaps inadequate nutrition, and many other factors to lay the groundwork for the implantation of the tubercle bacillus to cause tuberculosis (after all, we are all exposed to this germ, but we don't all develop galloping consumption), so it takes many factors to result in skin disorders. Again, as with all psychosomatic disorders, it is a matter of degree. The emotional disturbance may play an important role or a minor role.

The skin as an organ of expression

When you blush, you are expressing an emotion. Your skin is the organ of expression. When you go pale with anxiety or fear, it is your skin that is speaking its "organ language." When you flush beet-red with anger, it is again your skin that speaks for you. It speaks for you when you are embarrassed, disturbed, under stress, ashamed, fearful, angry, excited—inmost stress situations, regardless of cause. It is an important organ of expression since it is exposed for all the world to see, and we know it.

We, each of us, live in our own skin envelope, and it is difficult to communicate with any other skin envelope and its contents. This is just another way of saying that the skin is an organ to isolate us from our environment, including other people. But it is also an organ to put us into contact with others and with all parts of our environment. When we were caressed, fondled, babied, loved, at various stages of our lives, it was our skin that was caressed, fondled, and loved. Skin love is expressed in the colloquial, "love is skin deep" expression. We speak of our beloved's complexion as being "fair," her skin "delicate and soft," her "peaches and cream" complexion, and direct many other poetic expressions toward the skin.

It is obvious that our skin is an organ of expression, love, contact with our fellows, as well as an organ for the protection and isolation of our body. The skin occupies a role very much like the mouth, in being the earliest site for the expression of love. It is little wonder that it is the site of psychosomatic disorders such as nervous eczema, acne, rectal or vaginal itch, and others.

What is neurodermatitis?

This mouth-filling term refers to nervous eczema as distinguished from the eczema that follows contact with an irritating substance. Usually, we think of the eczema-neurodermatitis group of skin disorders, lumping them all together. But if we want to separate out the skin disorders that are primarily emotional in origin, we would have to speak of the *nervous eczema cases* as being distinct from the *contact eczema* problems. For our purposes, however, it is best to abandon all such labels and think only of skin disturbances primarily or secondarily related to our emotions as psychosomatic. We will speak of neurodermatitis and eczema only because these are commonly accepted terms, and you may hear them from your physician.

John was a difficult problem case. He was 18 and had a severe eczema-like skin condition of his face. To quote him, "my face looks a mess." This condition developed when he told his parents that he was going to "get married," and they told him that, if he did, he would have to leave home and support himself and his wife with no help from them. This is a very common problem these days, youngsters wanting to get married long before they are prepared to assume full responsibility for this important step. His parents correctly considered him too young for marriage, too little prepared financially, too immature, and said the same for his proposed bride.

This made John even more nervous than usual (he was always "very sensitive and easily disturbed," as shown by his Conflict Check Chart), and he then developed blisters on his lips. A nervous twitch appeared at the corner of his left eye, and this disturbed him almost as much as his appearance.

John was quite honest with himself when he worked out his Conflict Check Chart, and recognized his own areas of immaturity. He saw the relationship between his skin condition and his conflict with his "folks." He recognized that his skin was speaking the organ language of fear and worry and protest in this rebellion against parental authority.

Guided Association sessions in the privacy of his own home, combined with Substitute Aggression sessions directed against his parents, cleared away the repressed emotions, and the skin stopped its protest. Without any medication at all, his skin condition cleared rapidly. This was clearly a dermatitis resulting from a psychosomatic, family conflict stress. The eye twitch persisted for several weeks beyond the clearing of the skin. Naturally, John and his fiancée agreed to wait until they were both through school and better prepared financially.

Nervous versus contact dermatitis

It is not always easy for your doctor to distinguish nervous from contact skin inflammation. Sometimes there will be obvious emotional stress, and yet the problem may be due to sensitivity to irritating cosmetics, industrial poisons, something in the home or place of business, chemicals, or some other factor. You must not try to clear up skin irritations by yourself, and you must not treat yourself with any advertised lotions, creams, ointments, or in any other way. You may prove to be sensitive to the medicine you choose, and make the condition that much worse. It is always best to consult your family doctor or a skin specialist. If no contact irritant is at the root of your problem, you may safely concentrate on the emotional factors, using the various methods in this book (*See* Chapters 4 and 5, and the basic FOUR-STEP METHOD).

Acne and the adolescent

This is the most common of all skin conditions, and the most troublesome for many adolescents. It shames them, and they often consider it evidence of immaturity and inadequate sexual development. It does seem true that acne is related to both emotional and sex gland development. It appears at the time of puberty, and may continue on after that time. It often seems connected with delayed emotional and sexual development.

Young ladies who develop this distressing affliction may also be anxious about their delayed or irregular menstrual difficulties. It is certainly true that many of these skin problems clear up spontaneously when the menstrual flow becomes regular.

It is obvious that in both boys and girls we are dealing once again with multiple causation. And we are certainly seeing an eloquent form of *skin organ language*. It is the protest of the budding emotions, the imprisoned sexual drive, speaking through the autonomic nervous system, the endocrine glands and the skin. The Silent Level of the emotions breaks its silence with this form of skin organ language.

Mary was 21, an age well beyond the time we consider usual

for puberty. But she had not yet menstruated regularly, and often skipped many months with no sign of her period. She had an advanced, scarred acne, and was emotionally disturbed by this, as we would naturally expect. The condition had troubled her for over seven years. She had consulted many doctors, and had used all kinds of skin treatments, even those advertised in the newspapers and those advised by helpful pharmacists. They all seemed to give some temporary relief, and then the condition became worse.

She also complained of headaches, a general weakness, and she tired very easily. Whatever the original cause, she now had a badly damaged skin, and I advised consultation with a dermatologist with a view to skin planing. This simple operation was performed with good results.

Mary had still another problem, however, and it was closely related to her acne. The Conflict Check Chart showed that she was convinced that "marriage is the best cure for acne." She realized that she could not yet marry, and she had a terrible sense of guilt over her sex desires. She even worried about her very innocent "petting." She had many arguments with her mother and could not talk to her father "about anything." She felt isolated and rejected by her parents and a misfit in her own society. Her girl friends were getting engaged and married, and she cried whenever she went to one of these celebrations.

All of these anxieties did her skin no good. She broke out even worse every time she went out on a date. Her backache and headache and constant feeling of weariness did not improve until she began Guided Association and Substitute Aggression treatment. She directed her aggression outlet against her parents, her dates, and her girl friends. Finally, she recognized the childishness of this reaction, and she laughed at herself for not realizing that the problem was within herself and not anywhere else.

When she reached this stage of treatment, her personality unfolded into an outgoing warmth, and she developed friendly relationships with others. Her symptoms disappeared almost like magic, and she was happier and healthier than she ever remembered being before. Although we cannot expect this result in every case, her new personality made her more attractive to young men, and she was soon engaged to be married.

Step-by-step, then, this young lady illustrates the full psychosomatic approach to these emotionally-based health-wreckers:

1. Correction of the somatic (body) factor—the scarred skin in this case.
2. The Conflict Check Chart, honestly used to look within yourself.
3. Guided Association and Substitute Aggression treatment in the privacy of your own home, to get rid of worry and fear and guilt behaviour patterns. You will naturally use Self-Suggestion and the Instant Relaxation methods as well.

Hives and the emotions

Hives is called *urticaria* in the medical textbooks, but a rose by any other name is still a rose, and hives by any other name is still very distressing. This condition may be due to a virus, an allergy, and to other factors, but there is often a strong *emotional factor* as well.

Nevertheless, you must not attempt self-treatment. Your family doctor may find the answer quickly, or he may need your help in clearing the emotional problems. In this case, you may safely proceed with the methods you have already learned.

Helen, a 24-year-old newlywed, developed hives on her back and "fever blisters" on her lips, during her wedding night. She had married the man her mother had selected for her. Her father was dead, and her mother had delivered an ultimatum: "Marry this man or leave my home." This was a harsh command, and Helen was an obedient but broken-hearted bride. The skin blisters, especially those on her face, were her "defense" against the unwanted husband. She obviously could not consummate the wedding night "obligations" with these painful blisters.

The answer was not simple. She would either have to adjust and make the best of a difficult situation, or annul the marriage and start out on her own. She had always been self-sufficient and had worked as a secretary to earn her own way through college. She knew that she could continue to do that to earn her own way without her mother. I did not want to make this decision for her, but we did discuss the matter from all viewpoints. Her own decision was to annul the marriage, leave her mother—whom she now hated with deep intensity—and to start life on her own.

The hives cleared rapidly after this decision, and she was soon in her own little apartment, self-sufficient and reasonably happy. But she now developed other skin and general complaints, obviously owing to feelings of guilt and anxiety. Headaches, general itch, and fatigue were some of these problems.

She started on the basic FOUR-STEP METHOD of this book. The Conflict Check Chart helped her locate the many trouble spots of her long-standing "battle" with her mother. Guided Association released her from these emotional depth charges, getting rid of their explosive nature in a harmless, controlled fashion. Substitute Aggression treatment, directed against her mother, helped enormously.

She became less hostile, less passive, and less dependent. She even changed her attitude toward her mother as the self-treatment progressed. I felt very sorry for her ex-husband, for he had acted in good faith and assured me that he loved Helen. Curiously, when Helen realized the source of her behaviour, she was willing to forgive her mother and even to see her poor, "short-term husband" again.

They both now recognized the fact that the hives were a defense mechanism and the organ language of a double hostility, the hostility toward her mother and only secondarily against her husband. The story had a happy ending in that they decided to forgive and forget and then remarried.

Itch and your emotions

It is now clear to you that an itching skin is a very common psychosomatic disorder. The itch can be a general one, covering almost the whole skin surface, but it is usually localized to the skin around the rectum or the vagina. Rectal itch is one of the most common skin conditions of all, and is usually mislabeled "itching piles." This condition affects literally millions of us—so many that drug manufacturers offer physicians and the public a great array of pills, salves, lotions, and other preparations for treatment. Since it is the basic emotional problem that must always be brought under control, it is obvious that drug treatment can only be a small part of the best approach.

One of my most recent patients was a 33-year-old housewife who developed severe itch in these regions. She had many problems that were clearly brought out by the Conflict Check Chart. There was never enough money, even though her husband did his very best as the manager of an active gas station. She did not get along with her daughter and had little or no control over her.

One of her major complaints was that her husband always came home "dirty," and she thought that she was being "irritated by the grease and dirt." "I wish that he would bathe more often," she complained. Her skin itch naturally provided a good reason to keep her distance.

The local skin problem was easily controlled by instructions in general body hygiene and cleanliness. I advised using a castile soap, followed by patting the area dry and then powdering with corn starch.

The basic emotional problem required several months of Guided Association therapy, following down the leads of her Conflict Check Chart. She soon saw that she was using the itch as a defense mechanism and as a rebellion against her husband. The condition cleared rapidly, once this became obvious to her.

She has continued to use Guided Association and the Relaxation methods to work out her annoyances and daily "gripes." The result has been "a revelation in how good a day can be."

How to control rectal itch

Since this type of psychosomatic skin problem is the most common of the itch conditions, I will take a moment to show you how to bring it under control.

1. Your first step is to see your doctor. If you have piles, inflamed pockets in the rectum, or any other local trouble, it must be corrected. Fortunately, there are simple, painless methods to do this in the office.*
2. At the same time, you must complete your Conflict Check Chart and your family history to locate your unspoken fears and worries.
3. You will then begin Guided Association and Self-Suggestion treatment daily in your own home.
4. Use the Relaxation methods, and get rid of repressed aggression by the Substitute Aggression practice. This will get the

---

* See my book, *Painless Office Rectal Treatment.*

violence out of your system—directing it where it belongs instead of against yourself. You will then stop tearing yourself apart (scratching).

I could give you dozens of examples of such cases, but if this is your problem you need only follow the treatment method as outlined. The rest is up to you and your doctor—but most especially, it is up to you.

Points to remember:

1. Skin disorders, like all other diseases, are the result of more than one cause.
2. There is an emotional component in skin disease, sometimes as the major cause.
3. The skin is an organ of emotional expression and speaks its own distinctive organ language.
4. Nervous dermatitis is due to emotional stress, but contact dermatitis may also have an emotional relationship.
5. Acne is often evidence of immaturity and inadequate sexual development.
6. Hives may be due to emotional stress, hostility toward parents or spouse, etc.
7. Itch is a complex problem, and the emotions are often the major underlying cause.
8. Rectal and vaginal itch are often emotionally based. Both can be controlled.

Chapter 12

HOW TO ANSWER YOUR ALLERGY
WITH COMMON SENSE

How to use chapter 12

1. Check this list and see if you have any of the following symptoms:

   Wheezing breathing (asthma)

   Hives

   Hay fever

   Rose fever

   Nose, throat, and eye inflammation—seasonal or when exposed to cosmetics, drugs, etc.

   Migraine headaches

   Allergic skin irritations or inflammation

   Food allergy causing diarrhea, bowel irritation or ulcerations, nausea and vomiting, other stomach or bowel irritation

   Frequent colds

   Frequent bronchitis

   Severe itch anywhere in the body

   House dust sensitivity or any other respiratory allergy causing wheezing or other lung irritation

   Allergic headaches, less severe than migraine

   Nose and throat membrane sensitive to temperature changes, such as exposure to air conditioning, etc.

2. If you do have any of these symptoms, read this chapter NOW.
3. Then, turn back to Chapter 4 and fill out the Conflict Check Chart. This tells you *why* you have these allergic, psychosomatic health-wreckers.

4. Now, turn to Chapter 5 and begin the simple Guided Association sessions right in the privacy of your own home. This will get rid of your underlying worries and fears—the roots of your psychosomatic allergy.
5. Now, begin the important Muscle Relaxation and the Self-Suggestion methods to learn how to relax all parts of your body, how to literally Switch Off Your Allergy Symptoms.
6. Practice the KEY WORD magic for Instant Action in muscle relaxation, instant pain and spasm release, and instant itch control.

What is allergy?

Allergy is a complex problem, representing a special sensitivity of our body tissues to some irritant. The irritant may get into our body through the mouth, a food sensitivity. Or it may be inhaled, causing a sensitivity reaction in our nose, sinuses, or lungs. In some cases the irritating substance may be injected by the physician, as is sometimes seen in penicillin reactions and reactions to other drugs. Our skin may be sensitive to all types of substances, sometimes those with which we must work in our jobs. Many women are sensitive to cosmetics, and special non-allergic cosmetics have been commercially prepared for them. Medicines to be used on the skin may make the condition worse, a skin allergy to the particular medicine. On the other hand, we may be unusually sensitive to substances coming from some infection within our own body. And finally, the hypersensitivity may be an emotional reaction—allergy to parents, wife or husband, etc.

Heredity seems to play a part in allergy, but so it does in all disease. We all have our weak links, and if our lungs are especially sensitive, the allergy may take the form of asthma. If our nasal membranes are easily irritated, we may express our sensitivity as hay fever, or even as frequent colds. If our skin is the weak spot, the allergy may be in the form of a skin inflammation, severe itch, hives, or some other symptom, running the whole gamut of skin disorders.

Allergy is psychosomatic

We are saying that allergy is psychosomatic in the broadest sense, the usual sense, as a disease of the mind-body unit. And we are also saying, as we have throughout this book, that allergy is not the result of a single factor, but rather of many things acting together to produce the body-mind changes the physician calls *allergy.*

In some of us the allergy will be primarily due to sensitivity to a pollen, like the hay fever of ragweed pollen irritation. Or there may be a special intestinal tract sensitivity to sea food, resulting in diarrhea whenever we eat such food. Or the problem may be in the lungs, the sensitivity being to house dust, our lungs reacting with bronchial spasm and the wheezing of asthma. But in other patients, the basic problem may be emotional, and the irritating pollen, food, or whatever, may then merely trigger an already volatile tissue or organ into an allergic reaction. There is obviously a total body-mind reaction in allergy as there is in all other disease, the variation being in the degree of emotional involvement.

In some cases, the emotional stress factor may be so dominant that the total symptom reaction will be on that basis alone. In others, the emotions will play a hardly discernible role, but remain well in the background. Sometimes this will be shown to be a more fundamental factor when Guided Association brings the repressed emotional conflicts to the surface. (*See* Chapter 5)

Are allergic people neurotic?

There seems to be a strong relationship between a generally neurotic personality and allergy. But this may be a deceptive statistic since there is so much allergy and so much neurosis. As we have already learned, it is difficult or impossible to spell out the meaning of "normal." Since we are all emotionally immature in one area or another of our personality, and since allergy is a very common condition, it is not surprising that we find so much apparent connection between neurosis and allergy. It would be even more surprising if we did not.

It is very easy to go off the "deep end" in theory, and say that the neurotic person is more susceptible to allergy. It would be better to say that the person with emotional disturbances, the individual with an unstable autonomic nervous system, the man or woman whose childhood training and environment left a frustrated, love-starved personality, is most susceptible to all psychosomatic disorders, including allergy.

How to handle your allergy

The obvious *first step is to see your physician,* and especially a physician who really understands this complicated problem. You should first discover whether or not there is a specific irritant at the root of your sensitivity. If your problem is house dust, ragweed, or rose pollen, this must be discovered. You will be improved in many cases if you are then desensitized by repeated, small-dose injection treatment. The very substance to which you are sensitive is given to you by these injections, gradually increasing their strength until you no longer react violently either to the skin injection or to the naturally-occurring substance.

But this is only the first step. In some cases, even though you may have all the usual tests, no specific sensitivity is discovered. You are then a candidate for the psychosomatic therapy methods of this book. Or there may be skin sensitivity to some substances, even though these same materials have absolutely no connection with your allergy. These can be real puzzlers to your doctor.

If you are this problem patient, you may require the combined services of the allergist and the psychosomatic methods of this book, especially as in Chapters 4 and 5. Since there are very few physicians trained in both, you would do well to learn and apply the methods of this book, even if your doctor does find a specific sensitivity in your case. Remember that the complete mind-body unit must be treated, and not just one isolated factor.

Treat the total person

Sue Ellen's case was just such a complicated problem. She was a hay fever sufferer, and her symptoms always came on during the rose-blooming season. So far so good, and very simple indeed. But—not so!

Practically every member of her family had a history of allergy. Her mother was a migraine sufferer, her father suffered from asthma, one brother suffered from a continuous nasal allergy, and her sister suffered intestinal sensitivity to chocolate and wheat foods. Only one member of this "suffering" family, a younger brother, had so far escaped the allergy problem. By this time, you have realized that the word *suffer* was the one continuously used by the patient. I later learned that this was her mother's pet word, and it had been adopted by the other family members as well. Whatever the problem, whatever the stress situation, they "suffered." As our Guided Association later showed, this was a key word for the activation of this girl's symptoms, even without roses.

This key word—"suffer"—went back to her early childhood when she "suffered" through each of the usual childhood diseases. She went on to "suffer" all the problems of adolescence, including painful menstrual periods, acne, and even "suffered" problems with her school chums.

She was sensitive to rose pollen, without a doubt, but she could and did have attacks of the same "suffering," the same allergy symptoms, even when there was no rose pollen in the air. Skin tests also showed sensitivity to various other substances, including house dust. But she had no symptoms when exposed to these substances. You must remember that your skin may be sensitive, but this does not necessarily mean that your body generally will be sensitive. This limits the diagnostic value of skin tests.

Genuine versus imitation allergy

In this case, we had a combination of genuine and imitation allergy. The rose pollen sensitivity was genuine. The attacks that occurred in the absence of such pollen were imitation allergy. This does not mean that she didn't suffer during these attacks, whatever their source. She did indeed suffer, and in that sense, both types were genuine. But, in one instance, the attacks were precipitated by an external irritant, and in the others they were triggered by her emotions, and by her conditioned reaction to the word and thought of *suffering*.

This is a pseudo-heredity problem as well as a genuine, inherited tissue weakness. Sue Ellen had exceedingly sensitive tissues, and these tissues reacted with hay fever symptoms to rose pollen. She had inherited this sensitivity, this allergy predisposition. And she also had inherited an unstable autonomic nervous system and had the sweaty palms, the flushed face and neck, and general nervousness to prove it. The pseudo-heredity part was in the attacks that imitated the rose sensitivity but were actually triggered by the family example, the family use of the word *suffer,* and the family tendency to actually "suffer" (in one form or another) during any stress situation.

The method for relief of this patient's psychosomatic problem included the following steps:

1. She was instructed to prepare a personal history in outline form, stressing the fears and worries of both past and present. She also was to prepare a list of family ills and causes of death.

2. The next step was to complete the Conflict Check Chart and to prepare a list of disturbing Key Words. *Suffer* was obviously the most important of the key words.

3. The third step was to advise her that she did indeed have sensitive tissue, easily triggered to allergic reaction. She was also convinced that the trigger mechanism could originate in her mind, based upon worry, fear, and reaction to words, just as easily as if she had been exposed to actual rose pollen.

She was reassured that she could be made well.

4. Guided Association, and particularly the repeated reliving of the times when she was exposed to the word *suffer,* were most important in eliminating her acute reaction to this word. She had to relive and *re-suffer* her childhood diseases, her adolescent problems and all other times of "suffering" before she finally became bored with the word and stopped reacting to it with fear, worry, and symptoms. This took daily sessions for almost six months. She improved rapidly as soon as she reached this stage.

During this process, she became very expert in Guided Association, and soon was using this method to release herself from her current anxieties and problems as they arose. This is the best way to avoid future trouble and illustrates the importance of using these methods every day of your life as a preventive measure.

5. Instant relaxation training helped her to control her symptoms when exposed to actual rose pollen or other irritants. Most of all, it gave her a feeling of security to know that she was developing an increasing degree of control over her body. This sense of SELF-MASTERY is an important element in treatment of any psychosomatic problem, allergic or otherwise.

A rose by any other name

Another example of this triggering mechanism is illustrated by a young man who had severe asthma, also triggered by roses. One day, he visited my office and began to wheeze when he entered my consulting room. He had seen a vase of red roses on my desk, and his wheeze was the reaction. His attack was quickly cut short when I pointed out that these were plastic imitations, very good ones to be sure, but not good enough to produce pollen.

The *sight* of the roses was enough to trigger a well-conditioned body mechanism, setting in motion the body forces that cause bronchial spasm and all the other symptoms of asthma.

Asthma and allergy

Asthma is a very common problem, and it can be very serious. I have seen youngsters gasping for breath and responding poorly or not at all to the usual anti-spasmodic medicines. Sometimes the asthma is almost continuous and we call it *status asthmaticus*. Some of these cases are fatal. All asthma patients are emotionally disturbed. The symptoms of this disorder are enough to disturb anyone, even if there were no underlying personality problems.

I have already told you the case history of the youngster who was allergic to his parents and survived only because he was sent away from home at 12 years of age. Such emotional disturbances may result from little or no love during the important formative childhood of the patient. They may be caused by abnormal emotional patterns during feeding training or in the total relationship between mother and child.

One theory is that there is a sudden threat to the child's security, a threat to the normal attachment to the mother. This is associated, in such cases, with repression of the normal desire to cry. Later on, there may be an imitation of the allergy symptoms when exposed to stress or threats to security, the wheeze being thought of as a repressed cry. Body language! Such repression of normal reactions during childhood may very well condition our body tissues, producing an unusual degree of sensitivity in those tissues. When exposed to irritating substances in the air, perhaps smog and its irritating particles or pollens, the tissues sensitized in childhood may respond with the wheeze and other symptoms of asthma. Remember that this is just a theory, but the response of such patients to Guided Association and training in relaxation therapy tends to substantiate the idea.

Asthma and the repressed cry

A patient who seems to confirm this theory was an asthma problem from six years of age until (and beyond) the time I saw him at eighteen. He had been given a very strict upbringing, his mother having died when he was six. He could not understand or accept this apparent abandonment by his mother, but he had been trained not to cry when he was hurt, and he did not cry when his mother "left." Even at eighteen, he found it difficult to believe that his mother had died. His reaction was a mixture of love and hostility, as if she had actually abandoned him and his father on that very day she died.

The allergist could find no skin sensitivity, and no specific irritating substances were discovered. Nevertheless, he was placed under his care. At the same time, I instructed this young man in the methods of psychosomatic medicine. He proved fairly adept at Guided Association, using the method at home. I also told him about relaxation of his muscles and showed him how he could feel better even during an attack if he put himself into a state of deep relaxation (*See* Chapter 5).

Perhaps most important of all, I showed him how foolish he was to react at eighteen as if he were still six years of age. I did not expect him to be mature at all levels, but it was certainly silly to remain a six-year-old child. He laughed when I pointed this out, and I then made it clear that he must come to this point of laughter or boredom when he lived through his Guided Association sessions. This is a most important point and must be achieved if the Guided Association treatment is to be truly successful at the emotional-release level.

His asthma attacks decreased in frequency and severity, but he has not been entirely free from them. Whenever he has been in a stress situation, he has had a recurrence of asthma. These attacks are always in direct relationship to the times of stress, and he knows it. Their severity is in direct proportion to the importance he attaches to the disturbing problem. Fortunately, he now knows how to control their duration and ultimate severity by using the relaxation and self-affirmation methods. And he can usually bring himself to the laughing or boredom stage with these current problems, using the living-through method of Guided Association.

You may use this method yourself, not only for the repressed emotions of your past, but also for the disturbing problems of the present. Just relive the distressing current situation repeatedly; this must be done in the present tense, until you come to the point of boredom or laughter, as directed for Guided Association. You will then be released from the current tension. Whatever symptoms may be associated with that tension will also be relieved. This is true for all psychosomatic disorders triggered by current stress, especially if your reaction to that stress is associated with deep emotional involvement.

Allergic headache

As with asthma, where we must ask ourselves—"fact or fiction?"—so it is with headache. Naturally, we do not literally mean fact or fiction, and we are using this phrase only to help us clear our thinking of the cobwebs resulting from the idea that there is only a single organic cause for these allergic problems. We might do the same for hay fever, asking—"Is it in your mind or in your nose?" But again, we would be making a serious mistake if we took the question literally, because hay fever is both in the mind and in the nose.

The same is true for the so-called allergic headache or migraine. The mind-body unit is responding, and the headache is a mind-body response to various irritating substances, emotions, or both.

Allen L. tells an interesting story that shows us the danger of a one-sided viewpoint in the headache patient. He had suffered severe headaches for over five years, and they were beginning to be "more than I can stand." The headaches were all on the left side of his head, a characteristic, one-sided, migraine headache.

When I saw him, he was 31 years old. He had already been through three years of psychoanalysis for "this and other problems." He had also been under general care for "nerves," and was receiving injections for nervousness. He told me that he had several medicine cabinets overflowing with headache remedies, none of which had helped for more than a few days.

My examination showed evidences of brain pressure (this can be seen in the eyes), and I referred him to a neuro-surgeon for study. Brain tumor was the diagnosis. In this case we see the great danger of a lopsided viewpoint and the importance of an open mind and a careful diagnostic study before starting any form of treatment.

Sarah, a 24-year-old housewife, shows the other side of the coin. She had migraine headaches, and had been told that they were the result of high blood pressure. She did have high blood pressure, but her headaches and her high blood pressure were related to repressed emotional problems. These troubles arose when she lost her only child in an airplane crash. "To this day," she moaned, "I can hear how she must have screamed." She had not been at the site of the crash, but her imagination provided a scene and a sound that must have gone far beyond any reality.

This proved to be a major factor in her high blood pressure and her headaches. There were other areas of repressed emotional dynamite, and I cannot say which were the most important in this problem. Release from the internal stress, especially from the self-created horrors of the crash, resulted in a lowered blood pressure. The headaches, however, persisted for over six months beyond the time that her blood pressure came down to more normal levels.

Neurologic consultation showed no other problems, so I advised that she become expert in self-relaxation and in self-affirmation control. She did both, and the problem of headache was gradually relieved. Can we say that she had an allergy to her own imagination, the internal sensitivity being based upon the reality of the plane crash and her personal tragedy? This is a loose use of the term allergy, but acceptable from the psychosomatic viewpoint of a mind-body, sensitivity reaction. Certainly we can be sensitive to emotional problems. If sensitivity is allergy, then the term is justified.

Allergy and the common cold

I will now tell you how to make the common cold uncommon for you. First, you must understand that the common cold is due to a combination of factors. One of them is a lowered resistance. Your resistance may be lowered generally or locally, in the nose and upper respiratory passages. It may be lowered by poor food, poor living conditions, exposure to inclement weather, inadequate housing, improper clothing, air conditioning, and many other things. Air conditioning is one of the major "causes" of the common cold these days. We spend much of our time in air conditioned cars and homes and offices, and then shuttle from this artificial climate in and out of hot streets, non-conditioned homes and offices. The air conditioning itself is enough to sensitize and reduce resistance of our nose and throat membranes. The alternate hot and cold completes the job of sensitization, and the common cold, artificially created, is the result.

Viruses seem to be somewhat specific for the common cold, but there also seems to be the need for sensitized membrane before the viruses invade and take over. This sensitization puts the common cold in the allergy class.

And now for a curious revelation: Patients who have gone through years of conventional psychoanalysis often seem to improve their resistance to the common cold. They are less susceptible and have colds much less often than before the treatment. We can say the same for the abbreviated form of psychotherapy represented by Guided Association. This seems to show that repressed emotional pressures at the Silent Level of the brain sensitize the nose and throat membranes, acting through the autonomic nervous system. When these internal emotional pressures are released, the nose and throat membranes are no longer as sensitive, and local resistance to the common cold is improved.

The common sense approach to allergy

Whether your allergy takes one of the above forms, or is expressed as hives (*urticaria*—See Chapter 11), common sense dictates the following approach:

1. Seek an accurate diagnosis, being certain that your family doctor is aware of the possibility of both emotional and organic factors in your condition.
2. Consult an allergist and also a psychosomaticist if both are available in your community.
3. Learn and practice Guided Association, Relaxation, and Self-Affirmation methods.

Points to remember:

1. Allergy is a complex problem involving your total mind-body unit.
2. Allergy is a special sensitivity of this mind-body unit, the reaction developing in the tissue or organ at the point of least resistance.
3. The most commonly sensitized areas are the nose and sinuses—the hay fever reaction; the bronchial tubes and lungs—the asthma reaction; the skin—the *urticaria* (hives) reaction; the nose and throat—the common cold reaction; the brain-covering blood vessels—the migraine reaction.
4. Heredity must be distinguished from pseudo-heredity (the imitation reaction and the family-conditioned response).
5. Allergy, like all other psychosomatic health-wreckers, is a multiple-cause disease.
6. Always consult your family doctor and the specialist to locate all possible causes, all problem areas, and, most especially, your emotional trouble spots.
7. Your emotions may be a dominant factor, or may only play a background role.
8. Always treat both mind and body, and never one to the exclusion of the other. The mind-body unit is reacting when you have allergy, and the mind-body unit must be treated.

Chapter 13

HOW TO ACHIEVE
SEXUAL HAPPINESS AND FREEDOM

How to use chapter 13

1. Check this list and see if you have any of the following symptoms:

Guilt feelings about sex

Menstruation problems: excess flow or frequency, irregular periods, pain or cramps, missed periods, diminished flow or frequency, no flow accompanied by general disability, weakness, headaches, etc.

Fear of pregnancy

False pregnancy

Miscarriage or abortion

Vaginal discharge

Vaginal irritation or itch

Change of life (menopause): hot flushes, nervousness, irritability, tired, weak, and run-down, loss of sexual desire, fear of aging, depression.

Male change of life: loss of sex capacity, fear of aging, depression, frequent urination, fatigue, dizziness, hot flushes, poor erection, loss of masculinity, headaches.

Impotence

Poor control—premature ejaculation

Frigidity

Sterility

Pregnancy problems: morning sickness, food desires and other quirks, fear of labor, fear of death.

2. If you do have any of these symptoms, read this chapter *now*.
3. Then, turn back to Chapter 4 and fill out the Conflict Check Chart. This tells you *why* you have these psychosomatic health-wreckers.
4. Now, turn to Chapter 5 and begin the simple Guided Association sessions right in the privacy of your own bedroom. This will get rid of the underlying worries and fears and will release you from your symptoms.
5. Now, begin the important Muscle Relaxation and the Self-Suggestion methods to learn how to relax all parts of your body, get rid of spasm, Switch off Pain.
6. Practice the KEY-WORD magic for Instant Action in muscle relaxation, instant pain and spasm release, and instant itch control.

Sex mechanisms and problems

We will now discuss a most important problem area. Personality development, human motivation and development, and early and late behavior patterns are all largely based upon our sex drives. And it is the abnormal patterning of such sex drives that often results in psychosomatic health-wreckers.

In Chapter 2, during the description of how your personality influences your health, you learned something about your earliest sex patterns and those of your adolescence. In this chapter we will discuss psychosomatic problems of male and female sex organs and sex organ functions. We will separate fact from fiction on the painful menstruation question, and we will talk about the change of life and how modern medicine sometimes prolongs sex activity far beyond the usual time. The male change will also be described and discussed in the fact-or-fiction context.

You will learn about frigidity, the fear of pregnancy, the anxiety of failure and impotence. We will touch upon the fears of women during pregnancy, pseudo-pregnancy, spontaneous abortion, and the psychosomatic problems of labor. Functional sterility will also be considered.

Masturbation at all ages

As you already know, masturbation is normal. It occurs at all ages. It offers a pleasurable sensation and should not be associated with any sense of guilt. Unfortunately, there has been a great deal of nonsense written and handed down from parents to children, warning against the "dangers" of masturbation. But there are no dangers, except in the fear and guilt that result from such "authoritative" misinformation. If we hear it from our parents, it is accepted as true at the emotional Silent Level, even years later when we have learned better. The child thinks his parents are gods and that they can do no wrong. The adult finds out otherwise, and even the adolescent knows better. But the battle between our intellect and our emotions goes on forever, and the emotions *always* win. That is how psychosomatic problems develop. They represent the loss of the battle beween the intellect and the emotions, and the emotional organ language loudly proclaims the victory.

Harold illustrates this loss of the "emotions-versus-intellect battle." He was in his early forties when he became my patient. His large bowel spoke the organ language of ulcerative colitis, diarrhea, bleeding, general weakness. He had an enormous sense of guilt toward his mother, and he could not understand why he now hated her so. True, she had not breast-fed him, she had been very rigid and demanding in toilet training, and she had spent most of her time at "the Club," playing golf. But he had always admired her, and he thought that he loved her. It was only during Guided Association that his underlying hatred came out. It was then that he relived the time when his mother found him masturbating under the covers. She had screamed at him, "you will ruin yourself. You are draining out all your normal energies. Don't ever do that again!"

The incident seared itself into his emotional memory and rang down through his lifetime as his mother's curse. Naturally, he could not control the life forces, and masturbated often, even now that he was married.

During the Guided Association sessions, he finally recognized the rebellion of his colon as the organ language of ulcerative colitis, and his disease began to come under control. The combination of medications and psychotherapy helped greatly. At the intellectual level he "knew" that masturbation was normal, but on the emotional level his body-mind did not know. The rebellion against his "mother's curse" (his expression) was finally controlled, and he released this emotional dynamite to the point of laughter. He realized, both intellectually and emotionally, that he should not react in his forties as if were still a little boy. (See Chapter 5 for this method of self-help.)

Do females masturbate?

They do. But although all boys play with themselves, not all little girls do. It would seem that the ratio is about five to three in favor of the boys. This is curious since masturbation is just as much excitement for girls as it is for boys.

Perhaps the answer is in the fact that girls may be less apt to explore themselves, while the boy's penis is literally taken in hand every time he urinates. Nevertheless, most girls sooner or later realize that touching and fondling the clitoris and the vaginal lips is pleasurable, and they do it.

It is this lesser degree of self-exploration that may give some women a sense of moral superiority over men, a feeling of being better controlled, less aggressive, and, therefore, better generally.

If so, this is certainly only one factor, and in our rapidly changing world of male-female values, the growing role of the female in the male's world has changed this self-appraisal. As women take over men's jobs, they also take over the male sex standards, and so we have today's bachelor girl. In time, as the new cultural standards for the female are handed down from one generation to the next—at least in our Western society—there will probably be an increase in female masturbation at all ages.

Helen was no bachelor girl. Her early training had been strict, and she had been taught that she should never touch herself or allow any of the little boys to touch her. But Helen had followed the normal patterns and had "played doctor" with quite a few little boys. She went on to a normal sexual pattern in her adolescence, and finally in her marriage. I tell of Helen, not because she had a psychosomatic problem, but because she did not. Not all of us develop guilt about our early deviations from the patterns demanded by our parents. Some of us adjust, make our peace with the world as it is, and live relatively normal lives. We can learn a great deal from this, accept ourselves as Nature intended us to be, and stop rebelling against these normal behavior patterns. Who knows best, after all, our parents or Nature?

Menstruation—fact and fiction

One of my patients suffered from the curious belief that she was being punished for masturbation every time she menstruated. She had no idea that her monthly flow was normal. The result was a monthly psychosomatic health-wrecker that put her to bed with severe cramping pain and general weakness. This usually lasted for three or four days.

Her treatment consisted of the following steps:

1. She was instructed in the normal nature of the monthly flow. She was reassured that there need be no serious cramping or pain, and that most women carry on quite normally during these times.
2. The Conflict Check Chart showed her the times of stress, fear, and punishment during her childhood and brought out the fact that she actually had been beaten with a ruler across her buttocks when she wet the bed.

   Her subconscious mind had associated bed-wetting with possible soiling during her monthly flow, and she feared this time. Severe cramping pain and the general weakness of fear was the result.
3. Relaxation and Self-Affirmation training gave her prompt release from her symptoms and provided much-needed self-confidence.
4. Guided Association rid her mind of the fear and pain of her childhood experiences, and she soon was able to carry on quite normally during each monthly period.

Menstruation is completely normal in the sense that it simply represents the natural body mechanism for discarding the lining of the womb if it is not used for a growing embryo. In other words, the womb's lining is prepared for a pregnancy each month, and if this pregnancy does not occur, the prepared lining is no longer needed. Natural processes then detach the lining, and the flow is simply this discarded tissue and blood. Some believe that a woman should never menstruate, and that nature intended her to be pregnant all the time. This is not acceptable in our society. The population explosion would then assume "A-bomb" proportions, for one thing; and for another, no modern woman would accept the idea that she should be pregnant throughout the child-bearing age. Further, menstruation begins many years before the average woman marries, again ruling out the rationale of constant pregnancy without ever menstruating.

There are many superstitions about menstruation, some of them individual family misconceptions and many of them traditional in custom or religion. Menstruation is not disgusting or dirty. It is not a "curse." It is not "my sister visiting." It does not contaminate anything. It is not dangerous to men. The menstruating woman need not suffer pain or punishment and need not stay away from men. Menstrual flow is not infectious or contaminating. It is not the result of a childhood injury, and it is not the result of masturbation.

Menstruation is normal. There need be no pain and no disability. The blood and tissue flow is clean and harmless. There should be no fear, anxiety, or distress about this normal process. Mothers should realize this, not only for themselves, but also for their children. They should set the example of normal living throughout the menstrual period. If they go to bed, moan and groan, and are irritable and unhappy at these monthly intervals, the developing females of the family will probably do the same when they begin to menstruate.

Menstruation and pseudo-heredity

In this imitation of the mother, we see a perfect example of *pseudo-heredity*. The child sees the mother during her "curse," in pain, in bed, irritable, perhaps depressed, unapproachable. She thinks that this is the normal behavior during the monthly flow, and she expects to do the same, to suffer the same indisposition when she begins to menstruate. She looks forward to the same monthly "curse," and that is exactly what happens. This is not heredity. It is imitation, conditioning, unconscious training by example. Her mother probably learned it from her grandmother, and so on, simply family example and not heredity.

Menstruation should not be disabling and need not be very uncomfortable. Nature's normal processes are not intended to disable us and certainly are not designed to harm the female during the all-important child-bearing age.

Helen suffered "miserably" with each period. She had been

taught to call this time "the curse." She had seen her mother "suffer." She not only went to bed with cramps, but went her mother one better and had severe headaches and diarrhea with each period. This brought her to my attention. Six months were required to re-educate this young lady and her mother. They had to be repeatedly instructed in the fact that menstruation is normal. They had to practice Guided Association to relive the first few times they saw their own mother's "suffer the curse." They had to give up the word *curse* and substitute *monthly period* for this dangerous word. It was not until her mother began to see the light and live a more normal life during her monthly periods, that my patient decided to give up her monthly disability, headache, diarrhea, and all.

This problem illustrates the need to re-educate and retrain both mother and daughter, using the methods of Chapters 4 and 5, as follows:

1. Both were told the facts about menstruation, and that this is a normal process.

2. Both were given Conflict Check Charts to fill out. Their Key Word lists included the words *suffer* and *misery*. The use of these words during Guided Association reactivated old memories of pain and distress and fear. The word *curse* was also of importance in revealing how mother and daughter had identified with each other, the daughter imitating the mother in her symptoms. This was traced back to her grandmother as a family word and idea.

3. Training in relaxation helped control the symptoms of cramps, and training in pain control helped dull the discomfort of these times.

4. Guided Association rid both mother and daughter of the anxiety-producing, fear-stimulating ideas and words of their past. They enjoyed these sessions in the true sense of the word, comparing notes and vying with each other in the control of their symptoms. The final result was very good, all symptoms being brought under control.

Why menstruation sometimes stops

Menstrual periods ordinarily start at about 12 or 13 years of age and continue until 40 or 50. The pattern of duration is usually inherited. But sometimes the flow stops without warning, a condition called *amenorrhea*. This is a psychosomatic problem, involving the emotions and acting through the endocrine glands. There may be a lesser frequency of periods, skipped periods, a decreased flow, or any such combination. This has been observed during times of war, when men were not available to the women. The flow became normal when the men reappeared, even if there was no sexual intercourse.

The emotional shock of bombings, concentration camps, and the other horrors of war frequently stopped menstrual flow. When life was threatened in this way, it seemed that nature simply shut off the natural, life-creating processes of the menstrual cycle. There is little point in preparing the womb for pregnancy when there can be no pregnancy. Conscious and unconscious "reasoning processes" of this type apparently take over, and commands move through the (involuntary) autonomic nervous system to the endocrine glands to stop the menstrual cycle. The command to resume is issued as soon as the stress is relieved and men become available once again.

The fear of pregnancy can stop the mentrual flow, especially if unmarried. Arlene was such a problem, and as soon as she was convinced that there was no unwanted pregnancy, she resumed her normal menstrual periods. This was a great relief to a young man I knew very well, for he was the one who had the psychosomatic disturbance of nausea and vomiting, the nearest he could come in male organ language to his idea of the disability of pregnancy. Both patients were promptly relieved of their psychosomatic disorders.

General stress, anxiety, fear, worry, or shock may stop the menstrual flow. There is an actual measurable change in hormone secretion during this time of suppressed flow. When the stress is relieved, either in the natural course of events, by reassurance, or by emotional release therapy, the hormone flow goes back to normal and the periods start.

The condition that is the exact opposite of Arlene's problem may involve stoppage of menstrual flow when there is a deep desire for pregnancy. There may actually be a swelling of the abdomen, imitating a developing pregnancy. It is quite obvious that menstrual flow is under the influence of our emotions, desires,

fears, and anxieties—all acting on the ovarian and pituitary secretions to alter their activity. What's more, the intestinal muscles
relax and distend, and the abdominal muscles do the same in this
sad imitation of a very much wanted pregnancy. Here we have
organ language in a most impressive and expressive form, the
entire body cooperating to say "I want a baby."

Painful menstruation

We have already described this problem at length. I simply
want to emphasize the fact that this is a functional disorder that
is very common. There is rarely any disease in the female organs.
But you must always consult your family doctor or his specialist
in female disorders before any self-treatment. Even if there is
some enlargement or displacement of the womb, the painful
periods may still be of emotional origin. A combination of causes
is probably the ultimate answer for many of the sufferers from
these disorders.

The organ language in such problem ladies often extends far
beyond the womb to include intestinal disturbances, headache,
general weakness, irritability, and depression.

Treatment must therefore be directed to the uncovering of
repressed emotional stress, poor childhood training, or inadequate
information on the fact that the menstrual flow is normal and
need not be painful. Training in relaxation and self-affirmation
therapy (Chapter 5) is very helpful. If the patient is imitating her
mother, this must be gently but carefully brought to her awareness.

Vaginal discharge and the mind

The medical term for vaginal discharge is *leukorrhea*. This is
usually the result of some infection or irritation of the vagina
or the mouth of the womb. But it can be related to the emotions.
I have in mind a woman of 38, just married although she had re-
signed herself to being a "spinster." She was definitely not the
bachelor girl type, having more or less "shunned men" and still a
virgin.

The irritating vaginal discharge caused much inflammation
around the vaginal lips, and she was so "sore" that she found
intercourse a very painful experience. Her husband did not com-

plain and seemed quite happy with his bride. The local condition was treated, but the discharge persisted and did not clear until the patient was convinced that her problem was emotional in origin. She finally accepted the idea that it was just her fear of intercourse that overstimulated gland secretion in this region. As she overcame this fear and learned something about contraception (she thought she might die "at my age" if she became pregnant), the condition gradually cleared.

The discharge was obviously the result of fear of intercourse and pregnancy, and the rebellion against her husband was on both a conscious and an unconscious level.

The treatment method was that described in detail throughout this book, especially in Chapters 4 and 5. In essence, this is the way you will proceed if you have this type of problem:

1. See your physician for a diagnosis and reassurance. In most cases there is a local problem that will need attention while you are bringing the emotional factor under control yourself.

2. Prepare your outlined life story with a list of your past and present fears, and a list of family diseases and causes of death. Look for problems similar to your own in other members of your family. You may be imitating them.

3. Fill out your Conflict Check Chart and prepare your Key Word List.

4. Practice Guided Association to rid yourself of the worries and fears of your past and present. Practice Relaxation and Self-Affirmation at the same time.

The irregular menstrual flow

Some women do not have regular monthly periods. This may be due to endocrine abnormalities, some pelvic change in the female organs, emotional stress, or some combination of these factors. I recall one woman who disliked intercourse so much that she had a slight menstrual bleeding every time she was approached by her husband. There was little I could do for her, and this is the way she wanted it to be. Another young lady used such bleeding to escape "the drudgery of housework," employing a maid she could not afford. I suggested that since this was an unconscious mechanism (she had not been aware of the reason for her irregularity prior to Guided Association), she might do better to take the strain off her endocrines and her womb and do some of the housework herself. I also pointed out that the reduced economic strain on her husband might prolong his life since he would not have to moonlight at another job.

The change of life and your health

Life changes constantly, and change is the only thing we can count on, other than death and taxes. There are many changes in our lives, and some of the milestones for both sexes are puberty, adolescence, marriage and parenthood, the cessation of menstruation for the female, and the final loss of sexual activity for the male. Let us examine some of the facts and fancies relating to the change of life for the female and for the male.

Women hear so much about the change of life, the menopause, that they anticipate it even in their twenties. It is apt to come about at around the same age as it did for their mothers, usually in the forties or fifties. Those who know how their mother reacted to this ending of the menstrual flow are apt to have exactly the same reaction. If mother became very nervous and irritable, had "hot flushes," couldn't sleep, or was depressed, daughter will very likely have all of these symptoms. She may be simply imitating mother, "knowing" that "this is what happens in the change." This is very common. But we must remember that at least 20 per cent of all women going through this time of life have few or no symptoms. Are all the others suffering from endocrine gland withdrawal, the loss of ovarian hormones, or are they simply emotionally disturbed by the loss of their youth? In most cases, it is probably the combination of all three that is at fault.

These women need reassurance. They need to know that the change of life is not a sudden jumping off point. It only represents nature's gentle statement that they are no longer expected to bear children. Looked at from the other side of the picture, it means that they can now enjoy sexual intercourse without any fears of pregnancy!

These women need to know that there is no loss of sexual desire with the change of life. Just the opposite, because the freedom from fear of pregnancy often releases repressed sexual drives they never knew existed. It is sometimes hard for a man to satisfy such released female sex needs.

These women need to know that they will not suddenly grow old because of the change of life. Aging is a slow, gradual process, and it starts at birth. Good nutrition is more important to slow aging than any elixir, any single gland or womb function.

And finally, these women need to know that there are no characteristic symptoms for the change and that they need not suffer depression, irritability, or anything else. In most cases it is simply that they are doing what mother did, or what they have heard is usual for this time of life.

Joanne R. was going through the change of life at 51 years of age. Her mother had been "institutionalized" at 52, and Joanne believed that this was the result of the menopause. Joanne became depressed, and the depression deepened as her periods diminished and finally ended. This was a serious problem, but she was a very intelligent woman. I pointed out to her that she had never had any evidence of serious mental disorder. I pointed out that she must not identify herself with her mother to the point that she would expect to automatically have every experience her mother had had.

After all, her mother had lost three children, two of them in an automobile crash, just before her mind lost control. Joanne had no children. Her mother had made her own way in life since Joanne had been 12 and her father had died. Her mother was of an entirely different structure—short, stout, taciturn, withdrawn, and, yet, made aggressive by the necessity of earning her own living and providing for her children. Joanne was happily married and quite independent. She was an extrovert. She was, in short, quite another person, entirely different from her mother. Her reactions were therefore bound to be different since it is structure that determines our basic capacity for all types of reactions.

This type of re-education, Guided Association, relaxation therapy and self-suggestion (*See* Chapters 4 and 5) were all helpful in seeing her over the menopause hurdles.

Gland treatment for the change of life

Some doctors now advise the use of female hormones to postpone the change of life almost indefinitely. There is no serious objection to taking such hormones since modern statistics no longer seem to show a relationship between the artificial female hormones and breast cancer. We all value youth and good health. The fact that the cosmetic and beauty parlor business runs into astronomical figures each year shows the value women place upon both youth and the appearance of youth. Since this fear of aging (and the loss of the husband to younger competition) may cause many psychosomatic health-wreckers, it is important to use every possible weapon in the war against such fear. The estrogenic hormone is such a weapon, and these hormones may be taken by mouth or by injection.

The male menopause—fact or fiction?

Just like the female menopause, the male change of life is partly fact and partly fiction. Glandular activity slows down in the male just as it does in the female, but there is no dramatic signpost for the male to compare with the stopping of the menstrual flow.

Most of the symptoms supposed to be due to the male change of life are actually due to anxiety of a general type or fear of growing old. They include a decreased desire for sexual intercourse. There may be frequent urination and the need to get up several times during the night to pass water. Some men speak of hot flushes, dizziness, weakness, easy fatiguability, and a general desire to withdraw from the demands of life.

The difficulty in consummating the sex act may be due to anxiety and fear of failure. The urinary frequency is due to the normal enlargement of the prostate gland, an enlargement that occurs in most men as they grow older. But this has nothing whatever to do with loss of sex potency. The other symptoms are those you will recognize as common to all anxiety states, common to all psychosomatic health problems.

It is important and soul-satisfying to the male ego to realize that fertility is possible well into old age. The same is true for the consummation of the sex act. And by contrast with the moustache of the elderly woman, the flabby breasts, the deeper voice, men do not ordinarily show signs of loss of masculinity. But there is such a thing as a male change of life, and it can be proven by hormone studies.

Still, the symptoms outlined above are actually those of anxiety and are not due to the hormone changes. Harry R. thought

he was going through the change of life and became very despondent. He didn't want to live if he had to "be a eunuch." But
Harry was far from becoming a eunuch, for he became a father
at 83! Unfortunately, the woman was not his wife, and he insisted
on a divorce and remarriage to the 49-year-old woman who was
bearing his child.

Prior to that escapade, he had suffered severe headaches,
dizziness, had lost all desire to do anything but sleep or watch
television. When he became a father, proving his potency and
fertility, he regained his vigor, lost his headaches, and was an
altogether different man. I do not recommend this as the treatment for this psychosomatic health-wrecker, but it does illustrate
the strong emotional component, the anxiety, in the so-called male
menopause.

If you are worried about the change of life, be reassured that
there is a male sex hormone. It must be used with great care and
understanding by your physician since there may be side-effects.
It is also sometimes possible to extend potency by careful attention to diet, eating as little as possible, and choosing the right
foods. But most important of all is the realization that you are
probably not going to be seriously hampered in your sex life
unless you are well into your eighties or already over ninety years
of age. Besides, don't you agree with George Bernard Shaw that
it is good to be finally freed from the "tyranny of sex"?

Impotence—a psychosomatic health-wrecker . . .

A man may be potent and still get little pleasure from sexual
intercourse. This will result in either a burst of Casanova-like
activity in the search for a satisfaction he never achieves or the
relative abandonment of sex as not very satisfying—the anticipation was greater than the realization. These men do not love
women as much as they thought they did, and a loss of potency
may gradually develop.

Then, there are those men who are afraid of intercourse and
think that it drains their vital forces, their energy. They do not
seek sex very actively and may be great disappointments to their
wives. Gradual impotency is often the result. I had such a patient
who complained that his wife was frigid! Of course, the reverse

was the truth, and the problem was only resolved by divorce. His wife wanted more from marriage, and she went out to get it.

The psychosomatic health-wreckers that develop in such cases involve every body system. These men often become very irritable and demanding and have frequent headaches.

These emotional problems can be treated, and these unhappy men should find a doctor who is interested enough to help them find and release their emotional blocks. This will make for a happier marriage, as well as a happier man. It is essential to treat the wife at the same time, in any case, since the woman's reaction to such sexual inadequacy may make the problem even worse. She must be very understanding and very cooperative if the partially potent man is to be helped.

The treatment pattern is as follows, regardless of the precise symptoms:

1. See your doctor to rule out organic problems. He will correct these and give you the reassurance you need.
2. Then, outline your personal and family history of illness and deaths, to locate personal and family patterns of disease and fears.
3. Now, fill out your Conflict Check Chart. This will help you locate the source of your psychosomatic complaints. Key Words will also help, and you should search for these as you fill out your Chart.
4. You will then begin the practice of Guided Association, combined with Deep Relaxation and Self-Affirmation.

This is to be a daily and permanent part of your pattern of living. The psychosomatic symptoms in such cases strike at every part of the body, and may include headaches, irritability, general depression, and similar complaints. It will take time to get rid of them all, but, in the process, you will become more alive, more alert, more aware of the world about you, and you will enjoy life more.

Infertility and the mind

We all know families where there were no pregnancies until the apparently sterile couple had adopted one or more children. The sterility had been a psychosomatic problem, perhaps resulting from an unconscious fear of pregnancy while yearning for children on the conscious, intellectual level. Once again, in a battle between the unconscious emotions and the intellect, the emotions win the battle. But when the problem is solved by adoption, the emotional guard is down, the sperm slip in, and pregnancy results.

There is no doubt that peace of mind, relative freedom from anxiety, and the general ability to relax are all important in overcoming sterility if there is no organic problem. Naturally, the first step in the management of such cases is a study of both the marriage partners. At least one third of all such problems are psychosomatic, with the emphasis on the emotions.

Sterility and frigidity may go together, both based on emotional blocks. When unblocked by teaching, relaxation, and Guided Association, such couples may have babies without difficulty. They also have much happier sex lives, as well as improved personality patterns.

One such couple "never enjoyed sleeping together" because they shared their home with their wife's parents. They never could be sure that they were really alone, and they could not relax during their love play. This led to less and less intercourse, and they finally concluded that they were sterile and "would never have a baby." I suggested that they go away for a long vacation or get an apartment for her parents or themselves so they could have proper privacy. I pointed out the importance of relaxation and privacy during intercourse, so that the sperm and the ovum could meet in a peaceful, happy atmosphere. They tried the vacation. Pregnancy did not result, but they did discover that they were well matched sexually and were not "getting impotent." This was an important discovery and it led to the next step. They put her parents into a small apartment and were wise enough to tell them why. They understood and approved since they also wanted grandchildren. The result was good, and the first of three babies was soon on its normal way.

Pregnancy and psychosomatic disorders

You have already learned some of the emotionally charged problems that may arise from the fear of pregnancy. Impotence in the male, sterility in the female, rejection of sexual intercourse and open hostility toward the husband are often evidence of an unspoken fear of pregnancy. It is normal to be afraid of childbirth. If this is one of your fears, be at ease—you are normal. But it is also true that modern methods in obstetrics and modern germ-killers and antibiotics make childbirth very safe these days. If you are afraid, however, and shy away from sexual contact with your spouse, you ought to see your doctor for help. He will provide the reassurance you need. You can then practice the relaxation methods, for these will not only help you now, but will be of enormous value during the actual delivery of your baby. Muscle relaxation and self-anesthesia are two of the mainstays of modern delivery methods. Both are available to you in this book.

Having a baby is normal. In primitive societies women had their babies and then returned to work in the fields. This is normal. It is not normal to become an invalid, to be pampered and fawned over, or to feel that you have given your all for God and your country, to say nothing of your husband. This is the normal female function that you were created for.

Nausea and vomiting often distress the early stages of pregnancy. This is due to a combination of factors, the emotions and expectation playing a large part. Women generally expect "morning sickness," and we usually get what we expect.

To some extent, there are physical reasons for this, but unconscious fear of pregnancy, and unwanted and resented pregnancy, and other emotional pressures may use the intestinal organ language of rejection—nausea and vomiting. You cannot vomit up your baby, and you really shouldn't want to. Practice relaxation each morning upon arising and the self-suggestion that you are *feeling fine—better and better, every day, in every way.*

The psychosomatic problem of false pregnancy is a disturbing puzzler. We mentioned it earlier when we discussed the way menstrual flow sometimes is stopped by the emotions. Here we have a woman who desperately wants to be pregnant. Her body responds by stopping her menstrual flow and by distending her abdomen. Women think that they carry their baby in the "stomach," and do not distinguish this from the womb. And so the feeling zone of the brain sends out orders to the stomach to swell up, since there is a baby growing there. It is interesting how this confusion in the language of anatomy causes vomiting in the woman who wants to reject a baby (from her stomach!) and swelling for the woman who anxiously wants to have a baby. But these same women may also duplicate other evidences of pregnancy, with morning nausea, and even enlargement of the breasts, deeper coloring around the nipples, and, perhaps, milk secretion. Amazing, isn't it, how the mind dictates to the body! But it is not surprising to us, since we now realize that mind and body are one and indivisible. This is the keystone of psychosomatic medicine.

This control of the body-mind unit, sometimes motivated by unconscious desires to destroy, may even cause spontaneous abortion if the pregnancy is unwanted. The hostility may be unconscious, or at the level of our awareness, or a combination of both. Love and hate are opposite sides of the same coin, and normal for all of us. So it is not unexpected that the pregnant girl may both desire and not desire her pregnancy. Combine this with fear of delivery, and we may have part of the answer to the early loss of the baby.

One of my colitis patients, under the care of a psychiatrist for the past five years, has never carried her pregnancy beyond the first three months. She says that she is desperately anxious to have a baby and has been pregnant four times; but there is a deep uncertainty about her husband's fidelity, an open hostility toward him, and underlying anxiety patterns, for which her psychiatrist is treating her. He feels that her problem is self-induced at the unconscious level. I agree.

Psychosomatic methods to prepare you for labor

Just a few words on this important subject. First, having a baby is normal. You were designed for this by nature. As a matter of fact, that is all you were designed for. That is all your husband was designed for (in case you think this is a mere male dismissal of the female!). This is the pattern of nature for both men and women, the way the race is perpetuated. So, there is nothing to fear either from nature or man. Modern delivery methods are safe, and our hospitals are very well equipped.

Practice the relaxation methods of Chapter 5. They are at the heart of the natural childbirth method. Use the self-suggestion techniques to rid yourself of fear and of pain. You can actually shut off all labor pain with this method and have your baby without anesthesia. And finally, use the Conflict Check Chart and Guided Association to rid yourself of unconscious fears and hostility. This is the perfect combination for preparation for labor.

Sex education

And now for a final word on sex education. There is too much misinformation, too much mystery, and too much anxiety about sex. The mystery and the stress should be eliminated by correct sex information from childhood on. The time to provide this information is when the child asks for it, regardless of his age. Tell all you know (and I assume you will *first inform yourself* by appropriate reading about anatomy, physiology, and sex techniques). Your child will remember what he can and forget the rest. You can't possibly tell him too much.

Forbid nothing to him and do not have a list of books that are taboo. It is better for him to get his information from you and from the well written books on the subject, rather than from the uninformed gang on the street corners.

It is okay for youngsters to play doctor. How else can they explore each other and themselves? Do you have a better way to learn living anatomy?

Sex information should be presented by teachers of hygiene all through the school system, from kindergarten on, and into the colleges. The morals of sexual behavior are best left for the teachers of religion, especially since nobody listens, and adultery is the "parlor" game for about 90 per cent of our population.

The sex act should be a source of pleasure, a natural function, and not a source of anxiety, fear, concealment—a major cause of our psychosomatic health-wreckers.

Points to remember:

1. Our sex drives help determine our personality, our motivations, our behavior patterns, and many of our psychosomatic problems.
2. Masturbation is normal at all ages, and even during marriage.
3. Guilt feelings about masturbation, implanted in early life, may result in serious body-mind troubles all through life.
4. Both men and women masturbate, but men especially.

5. Menstruation is normal and should be expected and treated as a normal body function. It is not normal to have pain or any degree of incapacity with this normal body function.
6. Menstrual pain and other symptoms are often merely an imitation of the mother's behavior.
7. Emotional problems can alter menstrual flow, increase, decrease, or stop this normal function.
8. Vaginal discharge may be emotionally induced or aggravated by repressed emotional stress, even when there is a local infection or irritation as well.
9. The change of life (menopause) need not be associated with symptoms. It is a normal process, nature telling the female that she need no longer concern herself with having babies. This should be a great relief, a release from fear of pregnancy, and a time of increased sexual desire.
10. Gland substances can be taken by mouth or by injection to put off the change of life if desired.
11. The male change of life is partly fact and partly fiction. Male potency and fertility usually extend well into old age.
12. The male sex hormone may help you if your physician really thinks you need it.
13. Loss of potency and sterility (in both sexes) are usually largely emotional problems, and can be corrected.
14. The same is true for frigidity—both male and female.
15. The fear of pregnancy may cause many psychosomatic disorders, including frigidity and sterility.
16. Morning sickness during pregnancy can usually be controlled by psychosomatic methods.
17. False pregnancy is a perfect example of organ and body language crying out for a baby.
18. Spontaneous abortion is psychosomatic and can be helped by the methods of psychosomatic medicine.
19. The psychosomatic methods of Chapter 5 are very important if you are going to have a baby. They can eliminate labor pain and fear.
20. Sex education must begin when it is asked for, regardless of the child's age; and it should continue in the grade schools, high schools, and colleges. This will help eliminate many of our psychosomatic health-wreckers.

Chapter 14

VANQUISHING NERVE-INDUCED ILLNESS

How to use chapter 14 . . .

1. Check this list and see if you have any of the following symptoms:

Insomnia
Easily tired
Anxiety
Constant worry
Constant fear
Depression
Weakness
Headaches
Constant fatigue
Dizziness
Intestinal nervous reactions (*See* Chapter 6): nausea and vomiting, diarrhea or constipation, cramps and bleeding, ulcer or perforation.
Bone and Joint nervous reactions (*See* Chapter 10): pains and aches, arthritis, rheumatism, back pains, muscle spasms, and cramps.
Heart and Blood vessel nervous reactions (*See* Chapter 7): chest pain or other discomfort; difficult breathing—especially after exertion; worry over heart disease, a "murmur," or other complaint; headache or dizziness.
Nose, throat, and lung nervous reactions (*See* Chapter 12): wheezing; hay fever; nose and throat inflammation—seasonal, drug, or cosmetic exposure; frequent colds.

Skin nervous reactions (*See* Chapter 11): acne, itch, hives, nervous inflammation.

Gland nervous symptoms (*See* Chapter 9): jittery and excitable, tire easily and depression, eat too much or too little.

Sex organ nervous symptoms (*See* Chapter 13): monthly period changes, change of life—male or female, fear of pregnancy or labor, frigidity, impotency, sterility.

Eye and ear symptoms of nervous origin (*See* Chapter 15): poor hearing or poor vision, dizziness, ringing or buzzing in the ears, squinting, muscle tic at corner of eye.

2. If you do have any of these symptoms, read this chapter NOW.
3. Then, read any related chapter, such as Chapter 7 if you have heart symptoms or Chapter 6 if your symptoms are intestinal, etc.
4. Now, turn back to Chapter 4 and fill out the Conflict Check Chart. This tells you *why* you have these psychosomatic health-wreckers.
5. Next, go to Chapter 5 and begin the home sessions in Guided Association. This will get rid of your concealed worries and fears, and will release you from your symptoms.
6. Now, begin the Muscle Relaxation method and the important Self-Suggestions. You will now be on the way to relaxed peace of mind—a priceless possession.
7. Then you will practice the KEY WORD magic for *instant action* in muscle relaxation, instant pain and spasm release, instant itch control, instant sleep, and so on.

You are now well informed in the integrated action of your body and mind, acting as a body-mind unit. And you now know that your mind is indistinguishable and inseparable from your body. You also understand the role of anxiety acting through the autonomic nervous system, endocrine glands, and the brain and central nervous system, to produce the disabling, psychosomatic health-wreckers. In the largest sense, therefore, you are already well informed in the causes, the nature, and the treatment of nerve induced illness, for all psychosomatic problems fall into this general category.

But we will now deal more specifically with insomnia, general anxiety, weakness, dizziness, faintness, general types of headache, and the more disabling migraine, epilepsy, brain artery hardening and its symptoms, stroke and the fear of stroke, and, most especially, the little strokes of advancing age as death takes little bites.

If you can't sleep

Sleep is essential. Our individual sleep requirement is variable, some of us seeming to need eight hours, while others do quite well on six or less. It is said that Edison slept only four hours each day. During sleep, our body revitalizes itself, recharges its batteries, so to speak. But the subconscious mind never sleeps, and there is a constant flow of electrical impulses from all parts of our body to the brain, whether we are awake or asleep.

Impulses reach our nervous system from all our sense organs, from our eyes, ears, skin, etc., in the form of electrical currents. These electrical currents flow through many millions of nerve fibers to reach our spinal cord. They then move up the cord to the brain stem and the brain cortex. The billions of nerve connections and cells in this thinking cortical region of our brain then analyze these electrical impulses and send out orders to our body in response to the analysis of information received.

Since this constant flow of information impulses bombards us most intensively while we are awake, it is essential that we give our nervous system some rest during our sleeping hours. To do this, we must isolate ourselves from the source of the impulses, usually in a darkened, quiet room. This gives our brain and general nervous system, as well as the rest of our body, an opportunity to rest and rejuvenate itself. This essential recharging of the never-sleeping brain is so important that if we lose sleeptime, many health-wreckers develop in all parts of our body.

What is normal sleep?

We probably do not reach the condition called "normal sleep" until at least an hour after we have "fallen asleep." The impulses coming from all body regions are cut off gradually, very much like an automobile engine that sputters out. This is proved by brain wave recordings that show gradually diminishing bursts of activity during the first hour of sleep. Even during the deepest state of sleep, the brain remains active, but the brain waves now occur at a rate of no more than two or three per second.

As you gradually pass from sleep to dreaming, a different type of brain wave appears—fine, small "dream waves." At the same time, there are eye movements just exactly as if you were watching a play. This is still further proof that our brain never completely sleeps and further evidence that sleep is essential. But how much sleep do we really need?

You really do not need as much sleep as you might think. The length of time that you think you need is really the result of an acquired habit. Since you spend most of your "sleeping hours" tossing and turning and dreaming at very light sleep levels, the probability is that our body actually gets no more than two hours of deep, rejuvenating sleep. This would seem to mean that your body probably *needs* no more than those two hours. The catch is that, in order to get those two hours of deep sleep, you need to remain in the general state we call sleep for a much longer time. And so, we have the variation in "need" ranging between two to eight or more hours. You *need* what you *think you need*. You *need* the sleep time you have been *taught to need*.

The simple and obvious test is in how you feel when you awake. If you feel rested, alive, and alert, and ready to tackle the day, you have had enough sleep. If you feel tired out, anxious, and worn even before you start the day, you will conclude that you need more sleep. But is this true?

Not necessarily. A short, untroubled, deep sleep will be better preparation for the next waking day than a long, troubled, anxious time in bed, whether asleep or awake. This is obvious when we remember that our unconscious mind never really fully sleeps, and troubled dreams, a constant state of half-asleep anxiety, may torment even ten hours of apparent sleep. These ten hours will produce a tired, weary man at the start of the day.

Further, and this is very important, *your state of mind* when you fall asleep determines how you will sleep and how you will feel the next day. It may even determine whether you will be well or ill. You have learned something about that in the section on self-suggestion therapy. You have learned that the best time to give yourself both relaxation and healing suggestions is just before falling off to sleep. And now, we come to the realization that much insomnia is due to the anxiety in our mind when we try to sleep. We are tormented by the events of the day, the mistakes of the past, and our fears for the future. This will either prevent or postpone sleep, or make for a very troubled and restless night.

The symptoms of sleepless nights

Insomnia may be a very serious health-wrecker. A sleepless night is evidence of anxiety, as we already know. As such, the insomnia is a symptom and not a disease. It may be associated with many other evidences of anxiety such as fatigue, headaches, depression, and weakness. It is hard to face a new day after a sleepless or restless night.

The underlying stress, often an accumulation of a lifetime of problems, may bring out organ language in many parts of the body. Helen, a 41-year-old housewife, shows us how insomnia may bring the body to speak volumes of organ language. She woke each morning with a splitting headache, a protest from her brain. She became nauseous and after breakfast she sometimes vomited—a protest from her stomach. Before the day was over, she had abdominal cramps and sometimes one or two watery bowel movements—a rebellion in her large bowel. Careful examination by myself and by a consultant neurologist, showed no organ changes to account for her symptoms.

When she took a sleeping capsule, and had "a good night's rest," there were no symptoms the next day. It was quite natural for her to attribute all her troubles to lack of sleep. But this was only a chain of events with the insomnia in the middle, not at the beginning of the chain.

The chain actually began in her childhood when she had a "very sensitive stomach." Her mother had told her this repeatedly, and she never had reason to doubt her mother. Indeed, she proved her mother "right" all her life, vomiting and having diarrhea with every one of life's daily problems. The insomnia was the result of a lifetime of emotional stress acting through her autonomic nervous system in response to her mother's description of her "very sensitive stomach."

The Conflict Check Chart revealed this and other childhood trouble spots, and Guided Association helped her get rid of this emotional dynamite. She was trained in muscle relaxation so that she could put her body below the head into a state of deep sleep within minutes of going to bed. It took longer for her to learn to throw the switch in her brain and turn it off.

Appropriate self-suggestion at bedtime finally helped her to turn off the brain and fall asleep. Most important was the pre-sleep suggestion that worked for her throughout the following day:

When I wake I will feel fine, alert, alive, relaxed, fully rested. While I sleep, my body will become younger, healthier, happier, in every cell, every tissue, every organ. This will go on after I wake, and it will be easier to fall asleep tomorrow night. Every day, in every way, I am getting younger and younger, happier and happier, healthier and healthier.

You may use your own words to express the same ideas. You will find this more fully described in Chapter 5, and if insomnia is one of your health-wreckers, I would suggest that you review this important method at once.

General anxiety—our basic health-wrecker

We all suffer from anxiety in one form or another. Sometimes we speak of anxiety as stress, using the terms interchangeably. Stress, however, covers a larger area of body strain or injury than the word *anxiety*. But anxiety is a form of stress. It is the most common form of stress, acting upon us from infancy and, perhaps, even during our delivery. We are never free from anxiety, even during sleep. As you have seen, our mind and body is active while we sleep, as shown by brain wave patterns and by the eye movements while dreaming. Our dream stories are the product of our day's anxiety, and they sometimes reflect the anxieties of our distant past.

The anxieties of our infancy and childhood, the anxieties of our adolescence and youth, and the anxieties of our middle and later years are recorded in our body-mind as faithfully as if they were grooved into a record, transcribed into the electronic patterns of a tape-recording. They are there forever, every sight and sound, every odor, every taste, every thought, every fear, every tear, total anxiety pictures. And they are waiting to be re-activated by any similar word, sight, sound, odor, taste, emotion, or anything even remotely resembling the original recording or any part of it. It is as if the needle were poised above the grooves of a lifetime of recordings, ready for automatic replay at any time.

It is this automatic replay that causes symptoms that send impulses through our autonomic nervous system and out to all parts of our body. It is this automatic replay that is the ultimate source of the stimulus that starts our body speaking in organ language. This is the infant-child-adolescent-later years source of our psychosomatic health-wreckers!

Can all this be proved, or is it poetic license? It can and has been proved at the operation table, where an electrode is used to touch a brain spot, a spot that has recorded, for example, a time of a family gathering, singing about a piano. The conscious patient (brain surgery is performed on a conscious patient, and the brain feels nothing) is back again in his childhood, hears and sees, smells, touches and feels everything that happened at that time. The surgeon then moves on to stimulate other areas and other scenes and feelings. Every time he comes back to the first spot, the same scene is replayed by the patient—the same recording. That is the proof.

The symptoms of general anxiety

Since such a lifetime of anxiety touches upon an enormous number of incidents, many of them associated with violent emotions, the symptoms that result when they are replayed can speak through any or all body organs. And so we may hear the organ language of our entire body in terms of weakness, fatigue, depression, and a desire to give up and withdraw from the battle. Or there may be the organ language of the brain speaking in the pain and disability of headache, nervousness, and all manner of abnormal behavior patterns from neurosis to psychosis. Or the intestinal tract may protest with nausea and vomiting, diarrhea or constipation, cramps and bleeding, excess secretion, ulcer or perforation, and in many other ways. This is truly a sounding board for our emotions. We may be tormented by joint and bone pains, arthritis, rheumatism, back disorders—all are evidence that the back-breaking load of anxiety is getting to be more than we can bear. And so on, any and all parts of our body speak of despair, helplessness, rebellion, and the ultimate desire to call it quits.

What can be done for general anxiety?

This is a big question. Let me say right at the outset that it is good to remember that he who fights and runs away lives to fight another day. This old cliché is pure wisdom. One therapy for general anxiety is to run away. Run away temporarily, if you can manage, by taking a vacation. Run away permanently, if absolutely necessary, by changing your job, your way or place of living, your marriage partner, or whatever else it is that aggravates your basic anxiety state.

But before you run away, always *try to change the troublesome situation* by a logical attack on the problem. Study the situation, write down all possible solutions, and then discuss the matter with someone whose opinion you value and trust. If nothing can be done, you may then decide to back away from the entire problem by making a change in job, home, and total environment. *Or* you may decide that you do not want to give up and start over, and will *learn to adapt*. It is like an amputated leg; you can't start over to grow another one. You must adapt to the irreversible situation and learn to walk with an artificial leg.

The answer to general anxiety may lie within yourself. You may need to make a change in your own personality, your ways of handling a problem, your attitudes and behavior patterns. You already hold the keys to this approach. Fill out your Conflict Check Chart, locate the trouble spots of your lifetime, and release your emotional repressions by Guided Association. Do this with the help of your physician or by yourself. At the same time, get rid of your aggressions by working them out in action—swinging at the symbolic golf ball, punching the "offending" pillow or punching bag. Use Self-suggestion to alter your thinking patterns from a negative to an affirmative approach to life. Use this method to train yourself in control of your own body-mind and the reactions of that body-mind. When you do this, the psychosomatic symptoms will come under your own direct control, and you will be better able to adapt to the current problem.

I won't give you any case histories on this important subject. Every story in this book represents an attack by anxiety, regardless of the organ language being spoken.

Dizziness, fatigue, fainting, and weakness— what to do about them

If you have any of these problems, you must first see your family physician to be certain that there is no serious, underlying organic disease. Dizziness may be the symptom of ear or brain disturbance. Fainting and weakness may mean anemia, a low blood sugar, brain disease, or many other things. But once your physician tells you that there is no organic disease, you may begin to think of the emotional possibilities.

An unstable autonomic nervous system is usually part of the "faint and dizzy" picture. Hal, a 24-year-old automobile mechanic, really had a problem. He got dizzy and felt faint every time he crawled under a car. His sweating palms and flushed face and neck spoke of a highly sensitive autonomic nervous system. General examination showed no disease anywhere in his quite athletic body.

His blood sugar test was normal, and his thyroid function test (the protein-bound-iodine blood examination) was also normal. We had to look into his emotional stress patterns to find the answer.

Hal's father owned the garage, and Hal became a mechanic because his father demanded it. Hal wanted to be a writer. He had "always wanted to write."

"I feel closed in when I get under a car," he complained. "I feel as if the darned thing is going to crash down on me and smash my brains in." This was the source of Hal's problem, the reason for his dizziness and fainting when under a car. It was his nervous system's organ language, rebelling against his father's demands.

In this case, the solution was found in a discussion with Hal's father and mother. If they wanted their son to be well, I pointed out, he should be given the chance to show what he could do as a writer. If he did not succeed in this field—admittedly a very difficult way to earn a living—he could try other endeavours. But he should not work in the garage unless the choice was his own. His parents finally understood and agreed, and Hal was released from the emotional pressure and the accompanying symptoms.

Incidentally, it is practically impossible to faint while lying down. Fainting is the result of blood leaving the brain, and it does not easily do this while lying down (unless there is internal or external bleeding going on). I know a prize fighter who fainted while watching a needle being removed from his little boy's foot. The fear and anxiety had unsettled his autonomic nervous system balance, and the blood drained from his brain. The entire 200 pound fighting machine then toppled to the floor in a dead faint.

This can occur in any one of us, but is most frequent if we have led a sheltered life, if we are subjected to sudden emotional strain, and if there is a basically sensitive autonomic nervous system. You will recall that this is the part of our nervous system that controls our internal vital functions such as the heart beat, breathing, intestinal activities, etc. This part of our nervous system is most closely connected with the thalamus and hypothalamus, the emotion-recording region of our brain. That is why we may faint when suddenly plunged into a deep emotional crisis, an unfamiliar stress situation, or when some past fear is reactivated at the Silent Level of the brain.

Mrs. R.L., a 63-year-old mother of 3 and grandmother of 4, had such fainting spells with weakness and dizziness. She had "always been that way," she said. Indeed she had. A careful study of her history showed that she had used this device as a club over her own children to control their lives. They were always afraid that mother would die when she suddenly became weak, dizzy, and fainted during any family disagreement. She kept the entire family subjugated in this way. She had never really grown up, and she never would.

I told the family my diagnosis, and told them to leave the room when mother went into her act. I reassured them that there was no disease to worry about, and that there would be no performance if the audience left.

Headache and migraine—a psychosomatic protest

Headache sufferers deserve a careful general and neurologic study. Brain tumors may be overlooked, high blood pressure neglected, serious kidney or blood vessel disease missed, if these patients are not studied carefully. If the doctor says "all clear," begin to look within your mental self for the answer to your headache or severe migraine.

One of my patients complained of frequent headaches, speaking of them as "sinus headaches." She had made her own diagnosis because of a drip from her nose into her throat, her idea of sinus inflammation. There was no sinusitis, and it turned out that the headaches were simply her body language expressing anger with her husband. She had this headache every time they quarrelled, and since the problem was money, the arguments and headaches were frequent.

Another headache problem is seen very often in my practice when the patient is constipated and relates the headache to the poor bowel movements. In the first place, most of us are usually constipated; this is an American "disease." Most of us are hooked on laxatives. And, finally, constipation does not cause headache unless there is marked stretching of the lower bowel by an enormous amount of retained stool. The correct answer lies in the patient's *fear* of constipation, and his idea that headache is always part of the constipation picture. If he expects to have a headache every time his bowels fail to empty adequately, he will have a headache.

But it is an underlying emotional stress, perhaps going back to early childhood fears or of more recent origin in home or job, that is responsible for the protesting head. Sometimes the "boss is a headache," but more often it is "my husband who is a headache." The job may be a "headache." We all have our headaches in life. It sometimes takes the Conflict Check Chart and Guided Association mechanism to trace down and root out the emotional "headaches" of a lifetime.

This is well illustrated by a pretty little salesgirl, 23 years old and unmarried, who complained of headache and was always "just tired all over," every night during the working week. She was free from headaches on the week-ends and much less tired. If she had a Saturday night date, she was full of energy, even on Sunday, after being out half the night.

Her family history showed that her mother had "bad headaches," and her father used to say that his business was "one big headache and heartache." She had identified with and imitated her parents in her choice of symptoms. Her job was her "headache," for she had none during the week-ends.

The Conflict Check Chart and Guided Association traced down and rooted out the early times of fear, pain, and worry. She soon became quite expert in Instant Relaxation. This gave her immediate relief from her headaches, until she learned to prevent them altogether. Self-affirmation of general well-being—*Every day, in every way, I becoming happier and happier, healthier and healthier*—gave her release from her previous tired and worn out feelings. The major source of release was her realization that she had no serious brain disease, and that she was simply copying her parents in having headaches. This came during her Guided Association sessions when she lived through the times that her mother had complained of severe headaches, and the times when her father had literally gone to bed with his "one big headache and heartache" every time his business slowed down.

Here we see a good illustration of how anxious childhood experiences, with family-based symptoms being copied by the patient, were responsible for these symptoms in later life which were triggered when she started a job of her own.

Injury and lawsuit headaches

When there has been a head injury, it is sometimes difficult to know whether the headache is mainly the result of the injury or largely an anxiety, fear, or attention-getting mechanism. If there is a pending legal action, a "money headache" may persist until the case is settled. Since it is impossible to know whether the headache is due to brain or brain covering damage in such cases, or is an emotional retreat, or the organ language of the brain unconsciously acting as the ventriloquist for money greed, the patient must always be given the benefit of the doubt. At the same time, the problem should be explained very frankly, and relaxation therapy should be started. Since it is very hard to be entirely honest, even with yourself, when large sums of insurance company money are at stake, we do not expect too much in such psychosomatic problems until the case is settled.

Why relaxation therapy?

Headaches may be caused by muscle tension, and probably *most headaches are the result of muscle and blood vessel spasm and tension.* This is true even if the headache follows an injury. Such muscle and blood vessel tension can be found in practically all headache patients. And so it becomes obvious that you will benefit greatly from learning how to relax your muscles. Practice this relaxation for the muscles of the head, scalp, and neck especially (*See* Chapter 5). Practice also the self-affirmation method to release yourself from pain, and you will be able to reduce or eliminate headache pain in a very short time, without drugs.

Migraine—the inherited Headache

This is a severe form of headache, often found in more than one member of a family. This inherited problem often includes an unstable autonomic nervous system and other evidences of nerve sensitivity. Migraine attacks are periodic, and tend to "hit" one side of the head, possibly causing nausea and vomiting. In some ways, these incapacitating attacks of headache are like epilepsy. For example, the migraine sufferer may hear ringing, see bright or flashing lights, or smell a peculiar odor just before the attack begins. This is called an "aura," and is the way the patient knows that an attack is coming on. The same thing happens before an epilepsy convulsion. It may represent a local irritation of part of the brain, the sight center if the aura involves lights, the smell center if the aura is an odor, or, perhaps, the hearing center if the aura is a ringing or buzzing.

The migraine patient can't stand the least noise or other disturbance once the headache begins. He needs a quiet room and time to get over the attack. He may be very tired and depressed when it is over, or, surprisingly enough, he may feel fine and "ready to go."

Blood vessel spasm seems to be the reason for the headache and perhaps accounts for the aura as well. It may be that the spasm slows or reduces blood flow to the brain, irritating the special sense centers to cause the aura, and then triggering a further electrical spread of irritation through the rest of the brain. It is obvious that there is usually an inherited type of body tissue that is especially susceptible to such changes. And it may be that imitation of a mother or father, or the expectation of an attack when emotionally disturbed, may be part of the picture in some cases.

One of my migraine patients was a toilet-trained perfectionist, and his migraine was a rebellion against his long-dead mother, expressed during his adult life whenever he wanted to strike out against his "sloppy wife." He felt that women are "unclean and sloppy by nature," and he said that he often went into a "blind rage" and really wanted to "kill my wife." His was the only migraine in the family so far as he knew. There was no aura, except the "seeing red" of the "blind rage." The migraine headache was otherwise characteristic, with vomiting and a retreat to the "peace and quiet" of his bedroom.

Most migraine patients are emotionally immature—but aren't we all? They are often perfectionists, hostile from childhood on, at the unconscious level, and will never accept the blame for their own shortcomings. Sometimes, there is an actual allergy to some irritant (*See* Chapter 12), but most often the patient is allergic to his childhood training and parents, or to his adult environment or spouse.

If you are a migraine sufferer, take advantage of the relaxant drugs prescribed by your doctor to help you control your attacks. At the same time, learn to see yourself as you are and explore your past and your present for the irritating, repressed emotional dynamite. Release yourself from bondage to this emotional garbage (use the methods of Chapter 5), and you will be on your way to release from your migraine. Practice the all-important muscle relaxation methods, concentrating on your head, scalp, and neck muscles. When you feel the warning aura, go into a darkened room, lie down, and use the Key Word, rapid-relaxation method. When you are fully relaxed, begin the soothing, healing, anesthetizing self-affirmations. Most of all, you must finally *learn to take the blame for your own personality problems* and for every disaster you have ever lived through. When you have done this, really done it at the important Silent Level of your emotions, you will be able to stop punishing yourself with head-splitting migraine attacks. Self-understanding, self-control, and in the last analysis, *self-forgiveness*, will provide much of the answer to your psychosomatic health-wrecker.

The falling sickness and how epilepsy can be controlled

I knew a nurse who had increasing attacks of epilepsy over a period of 12 years. Drugs in increasing doses did little or nothing for her, except, finally, to produce a vegetable-like existence. She had brain surgery performed by an eminent brain surgeon after careful study convinced him that her condition was due to a local brain irritation. She was better for a time but soon relapsed to her former condition.

This condition became worse after she married and had children. The problems of marriage and parenthood were not for her, and she retreated into more and more frequent, severe convulsions. Curiously, marriage had been recommended by one of her doctors as "just what she needed." I heard him say it.

This is a complicated disorder. There is no simple answer, and I have told you about the nurse to illustrate just this. You won't find the answer in drugs alone, nor will you find it in psychotherapy alone. The combination may be helpful. In my own medical experience, if you have epilepsy, it is most important that you *lead as normal a life as possible.* Try to get and hold a job. Let your employer know your problem; hide nothing, and he will probably be understanding and helpful. Follow your physician's advice on medications. And finally, *practice all the methods of this book* to get at the root of any disturbing emotional problems. Rid yourself of these trouble spots in your brain so they will be less apt to trigger an attack. And finally, become very adept at instant, muscle relaxation. This may save you from serious injury in falling and during a convulsive seizure. It may reduce the severity of the seizure spasm and shorten its duration. Practice this relaxation all day long, every day, no matter what else you may be doing. Remember that the seizures do not ordinarily threaten life, and the disorder is nothing to be ashamed of. Alexander the Great and Julius Caesar had the "falling sickness," and they adjusted by conquering the world. You only need to "conquer" your own little world by facing the problem squarely and by living a reasonably normal life—no more and no less. Your condition will not get worse with time, but you must stay away from excessive drugs and depressing medications. You want self-control and not the life of a vegetable. You can lead a normal life, and you will start to do it as soon as you adjust to the problem and begin to change some of your personality patterns. The methods you have already learned, and will now practice, will help you on your way.

Death takes little bites

We begin to die as soon as we are born. Death does take little bites, and this is most evident when we begin to show the *brain-artery changes of aging*. Small, usually unrecognized "strokes" may alter our personality and reaction patterns. This may or may not be accompanied by high blood pressure. It is usually related to hardening of the arteries, often associated with improper diet. I have pointed out elsewhere that these changes are reversible, and that the hardening arteries can be restored to flexibility by simple diet changes (*See* Chapter 8, p. 141).

What is a stroke? This word is loosely used to mean closure or rupture of a blood vessel in the brain, followed by loss of use of some part of the body. But there can be lesser "strokes" when tiny blood vessels rupture or close and no paralysis is seen. Nevertheless, this is one of death's little bites, and the brain damage shows itself in changes of behaviour, changes of adjustability, all the changes we call aging. There may be dizziness, headache, insomnia, and we may tire easily. The mental pattern changes may bring us to the physician and perhaps even to the psychiatrist.

When the blood cholesterol level is very high, and if the patient shows the clinical picture that makes me think of such brain damage, I put the patient on my vegetable pattern diet. (See Chapter 8, p. 140). This is low in saturated fats and carbohydrates, and high in the polyunsaturated fats and protein. I prescribe a combinaton of one ounce of safflower oil, three ounces of skimmed milk, and two ounces of a tasty soda flavor mixed in a blender and taken before each meal. My patients call this the Cantor Cocktail. Hardened arteries are made more flexible, the patient becomes literally younger in many ways, and there is improvement both mentally and physically.

At the same time, since brain vessel spasm may be emotionally induced, these patients are told about Guided Association and the relaxation methods. The combination of therapy is the true meaning of psychosomatic therapy for a psychosomatic condition. It offers combined body-mind treatment for a combined body-mind disorder. This is literally life-saving and life-extension medicine.

Points to remember:

1. Nervous system psychosomatic health-wreckers include: insomnia, general anxiety, weakness, dizziness, faintness and fainting, headache, migraine, epilepsy, and the little strokes of advancing age and hardening of arteries.
2. You can learn to fall asleep instantly, even if you are now an insomnia problem.
   But—you probably need much less sleep than you think.
3. You can learn to go into rapid, deep, relaxing, refreshing sleep and awaken feeling well-rested.
4. General anxiety causes many psychosomatic health problems. You can learn to control and overcome most of them.
5. Dizziness, fatigue, weakness, and fainting can all be brought under control.
6. Headache and migraine are basically psychosomatic problems and can be controlled by psychosomatic methods.
7. Epilepsy is a complex problem, but the methods of Chapter 5 will help those who suffer from it to lead a more normal life.
8. Hardening of the arteries is reversible in many of us.
9. Little strokes of aging are often accompanied by, or confused with, emotional disturbances. Psychosomatic methods are of great value in such problems.
10. Your life can be prolonged, and you can become internally younger by using these psychosomatic methods of self-treatment.

Chapter 15

HOW TO CONTROL
EYE AND EAR AFFLICTIONS

How to use chapter 15

1. Check this list and see if you have any of the following symptoms:

   squinting
   poor vision
   night blindness
   eyestrain fatigue
   glaucoma (hardening of the eyeball): blurred vision, you
     see halos, dull headache, eye pains
   eyestrain headache
   flashing lights
   you wear glasses
   poor hearing
   ringing in the ears
   buzzing
   deafness

2. If you do have any of these symptoms, read this Chapter *now*.
3. Then, turn back to Chapter 4 and fill out the Conflict Check Chart. This tells you *why* you have psychosomatic eye or ear symptoms.
4. Now, turn to Chapter 5 and begin the easy Guided Association sessions in the privacy of your own bedroom.
5. Now that Guided Association has gotten rid of your psychosomatic eye or ear symptoms, begin the Muscle Relaxation and

Self-Suggestion methods. You will see better, hear better, and *be better generally*, as you practice these simple methods.

6. Then, you are ready to use the KEY WORD magic for Instant Action in muscle relaxation, instant pain and spasm release, instant itch control, instant peace of mind, and instant sleep.

Anxiety and your eyes

We often commit adultery in our minds, and the "sexual lust of the eye" was described by Freud. The eye is the entrance point for many of the most potent emotional crises of our lives. It is the eye that is pressed to the keyhole to see forbidden sights, the eye that leads us to our mother's breast, and to the breast cleavage and bouncing buttocks as we grow older, the eye that is symbolic of evil and magic. The evil eye, the hypnotic eye, the lustful eye, the come-hither glance—these and many more expressions of our colloquial language attest to the emotional tie between the eye and the forbidden world of sex.

This is one of the reasons for the psychosomatic problems of vision such as squinting, hysterical blindness, some forms of night blindness, the excess fatigue that follows "eyestrain," spasm of the eye retina blood vessels, and sometimes even glaucoma.

Arthur had many complaints, some of them relating to his eyes. I referred him to an eye specialist and was told that there were no eye diseases to account for his blurred vision that came and went, and no way to account for the flashing lights or the deep headache "just behind the eyes." He often awoke in the morning with this "eyestrain headache, just as if I had been reading all night in a bad light." And some mornings he vomited and could not tolerate breakfast. The eye specialist said that Arthur had normal eyes for a 21-year-old man and did not even need glasses.

The problem was considered to be functional, an *anxiety state* in which the organ language came from the eyes. The Conflict Check Chart showed many areas of emotional immaturity, especially in the sexual area. Arthur was a babe in arms about women, had never even kissed a girl, and derived his greatest sexual satisfaction from masturbation after looking at nude women through a tubular peep-show device he had bought in a novelty shop. He did this practically every night before going to sleep and said that he "needed it" to fall asleep.

The only nude woman he had seen "in the flesh" was his mother, through the bathroom keyhole when he was in his late teens. "It was hard to see much through the keyhole," he said, because of the angle of vision, and the "bright lights of a dressing table in the background."

Arthur needed much re-education, but first he was taught the method of Guided Association so that he could use this therapy at home. This helped to release some of the emotional tensions and guilt connected with his keyhole spying.

He was advised to make friends among his fellow workers, to start with double dates and later graduate to taking a girl out alone. The relationship of his visual troubles to his sex repressions was pointed out, and he was repeatedly reassured that his eyes were entirely normal. He did not accept this assurance until he had visited three other ophthalmologists. When they all agreed, he returned for further instruction and guidance from the psychosomatic viewpoint.

Glaucoma and the emotions

Glaucoma is a condition of increased pressure within the eyes and is sometimes called hardening of the eyeball. Without treatment it always goes on to blindness. Some glaucoma cases are congenital, an inherited eye structure problem beginning before the baby is six months old. But we are interested in those cases of hardening of the eyeball that develop without any apparent cause.

If you need to change your glasses often and find it hard to adjust to the new glasses, if you have spells of blurred vision and see halos, and if you have dull headaches and eye pains, don't delay. You may be developing glaucoma. Later on there will be night blindness and a loss of the range of your vision. See your eye doctor right now. I tell you this, and emphasize my advice by recounting the symptoms, because you must not trifle with this disease. If glaucoma is developing, you need expert attention to prevent blindness.

Such attacks may be triggered by emotional storms. A death in the family was the trigger in one of my patients. His symptoms were characteristic, and I referred him to the eye specialist for immediate consultation. He could not be sure, but later events proved this to be glaucoma. The emotional shock, acting through the autonomic (involuntary) nervous system, had altered the eye circulation and raised the pressure within the eyeball. The triggering event may be death of a loved one, sudden and drastic financial reverses, or more chronic anxiety states.

Even after eye surgery, these patients will be helped by learning emotional control. The pressure within the eyeball and the pressure of emotional stress seem to run together. This is a fine opportunity for the patient to help the specialist and himself by using relaxation methods, Guided Association, and self-affirmation to learn control and elimination of emotional tensions.

Looking versus seeing

We all look, but few of us really see. You look at your wife (or husband) every day, but when did you last *see* your spouse? We become lazy about *seeing* in the true sense of close observation, the sense of complete awareness. The result is that we gradually lose the ability to really see.

The same thing happens when we allow our muscles to go unused. They then grow weak and flabby, and we can scarcely walk a few blocks or lift a small weight without easy fatigue. Unused muscles and functions tend to waste away. The same is true for our eyes. When we become lazy about seeing and begin to look without seeing, our vision becomes poorer and poorer. Soon, we are dependent upon glasses. When we use this crutch, we make even less effort to *really see*, being satisfied with the magnification of the lenses. And so, in time, we need stronger and stronger lenses, designed to do what we have been too lazy to do for ourselves.

An extreme example of the way an organ wastes away with disuse is seen in fish who are born in underground streams, away from the light all their lives. They go blind although born with normal eye structure. The same thing would happen to you. When you make no effort to see, this is exactly what does happen, and your seeing capacity gradually wastes away. *The continued function of any body organ depends upon using that organ.* This is an important statement, and you should stop and think about it, especially if you are now wearing glasses.

Seeing involves much more than looking. To really see anything, you must use your brain as well as your eyes. Otherwise you are no more than a recording camera, perhaps only a mirror. To see, *you must want to see.* You must *make the effort to see.* You must think about what you are looking at. This is the relationship between vision and the mind at both the conscious and the unconscious level.

How to improve your vision

This leads us directly to a method for the improvement of our vision. If seeing involves the mind as well as the eye—and it certainly does—we can train ourselves to see better and more than we now do. First, of course, we must remove all subconscious obstructions to seeing. These are repressed emotional blocks against seeing, sometimes originating in our childhood. We remove them by the Conflict Check Chart and Guided Association.

The next step is muscle relaxation, especially for the muscles of the face, scalp and eyes. And then, our eye muscles must be strengthened, for we have neglected to use them when we "refuse" to see. We strengthen these internal eye muscles by using them, by looking and seeing. Look at distant trees or buildings. Really look and see the details of structure and color. Now look at something midway between this far point and yourself. Again, look and really make the effort to see details of structure and color. And finally, look at something close to yourself, the wall of the room, a chair, a picture, perhaps a book—this book, if you wish. Again, you must make the effort to really see. You must think about the structure and color, the detail of what you are seeing. Only when you make the effort to think and describe to yourself are you really seeing.

Now you probably begin to understand that you have gone through life, and you go through each day, without really seeing or hearing. You have been existing but not living, for you have shut off your awareness of the world. You are a camera, a mirror, and not a functioning body-mind. You are allowing your sense organs to waste away from disuse, simply because you did not realize that you see only a little bit with your eyes and mainly with your awareness.

Continue to practice these exercises several times a day, and always in bright light. Without light your eyes cease to exist; you will become like the fish of the underground stream. Practice moving your eyes slowly from side to side, straining to see as you do so. Do the same with eye motions that carry your vision and seeing upward and downward. Then try rotating your eyes slowly, stopping at various points on this rotary path to actually see in the different segments of the arc. But most of all, practice your far-vision, mid-vision, and near-vision seeing. Remember, this will do you little good unless you think about what you are seeing and make a determined effort to see more and more detail.

As you continue this practice, you will be astonished at how much better you can see. You may even be astonished the very first time when you try seeing without glasses and find that your vision is largely a matter of *mind* rather than lenses. Always remember the importance of bright light and the fact that the very existence of your eyes depends upon stimulating them with light. One final admonition—*don't use sunglasses*. You need the sun.

Seeing and expectation

If you expect to see poorly, you will gradually lose your vision. This is the *expectation syndrome*, for we get pretty much what we expect to get. You may expect bad vision because your parents wear glasses. You may have been told that you have "weak eyes." You may have started to wear glasses before you really needed them, *expecting* your eyes to go bad at a certain age.

Since vision is dependent largely upon your mind, your expectation will determine your seeing capacity. Expect more and you will get more. Now that you know the facts about seeing versus looking, you have good reason to expect more and better vision. As you train your mind to see, rather than look, your expectation will be fulfilled.

Spasm of retinal blood vessels

This condition can only be diagnosed by the eye specialist. He will see certain changes on the receiving surface of the inner eye, that permanent and reusable film we call the retina. These inner eye changes are due to blood vessel spasm, and they make our vision fuzzy. The blood vessel spasm is closely related to emotional tensions, again acting through the autonomic nervous system.

You already know how to get rid of emotional stress, and you should put this knowledge into action while under your doctor's care (*See* Chapter 5). The combination of treatment will be most helpful in restoring normal vision.

A final word on vision

The best treatment for eye problems, aside from that advised by your doctor, is to *use your eyes*. Stay away from rest and dark glasses. You need work for the eyes in order to strengthen them, and you need light if you are to see at all. No more sunglasses. The sun provides the best possible light. Indeed, this is the light that created your eyes in the first place. The Lord said, "Let there be light, and there was light." And this light was the sun. And if you shun the sun, you will lose your eyesight.

Your ear and hearing

Everything that I have said about your eyes applies to your ears, in terms of their function. We can speak of *listening versus hearing*, just as we spoke of seeing versus looking. Most of us do not hear more than a tiny fraction of the sounds about us. When we concentrate on the morning newspaper, and our exasperated wife sweetly says, "I smashed the car last night, dear, and killed two little children playing in the road," she fails to get our attention, and we say, "Yes, dear, how nice."

We hear, but we do not listen! Sound registers only in terms of a blurred vibration on our ear drums, utterly meaningless because we have not given it the attention of our brain. So, "yes, dear," to disaster.

Your own parents probably only heard what they wanted to hear. You do the same thing. It is our defense mechanism against the many problems we would rather not hear about, rather not see. It is part of the reason why we hear less than we should, and sometimes wear hearing aids we really do not need. Again, it is a matter of self-training in hearing, straining to catch every nuance of sound in music and conversation, using our mind to try to hear.

And the *expectation* of deafness at a certain age is also a factor. If you expect to hear less when you reach the "hard of hearing age" of your father or mother, you will indeed begin to lose your hearing. You will hear pretty much whatever you want to hear, and you will lose your hearing when you "wish" to do so.

This is not in denial of the organic changes that cause reduced hearing. Not at all. You must always see your physician and the hearing specialist for careful study. You may need surgery or a hearing aid to restore your hearing. But you may also benefit from the realization that you can, right now, hear more than you thought you could. And you can later hear even more if you will practice listening, perhaps using records. And you will hear still more when you get rid of your emotional blocks against hearing, blocks that may have been recorded on your brain at a very early age when you overheard forbidden conversations. There is no need to punish yourself now by shutting out the world. You are no longer the child at the door, the ear at the window or keyhole. Nothing is forbidden to you now. You may listen *and* hear, *if you try!*

Anxiety and your hearing

In addition to deafness of varying degree, *anxiety* may be responsible for ringing in the ears and dizziness. This is a late stage of stress reaction, since the usual organ language is expressed by the stomach and intestines, the heart, lungs and the other organ systems. When the ears begin to protest, speaking their organ language of deafness, dizziness, ringing, and buzzing, you are in a late stage of anxiety tension. And this type of stress reaction involves the brain as well, for dizziness and ringing in the ears, as you already know, is partly a reaction of your nervous system and only partly a response of your ears.

The first step in correcting this problem is to have your physician and the hearing specialist check you from top to bottom. They will be looking for inner ear problems to explain dizziness, perhaps a brain tumor, or some other brain disease. They will check out your blood sugar for the possibility of a low sugar level, or some other deficiency. If nothing is found to account for your symptoms, you may then begin to look within yourself for the anxiety roots of your problem.

Mary, a 50-year-old housewife, had dizziness, ringing and buzzing in her ears, and she felt that she would soon be as deaf as her mother had been. She took the first step by seeing her doctor and an ear specialist, both of whom assured her that she had no serious ear disease. Nevertheless, she was convinced that her mother's deafness was her fate, and she became withdrawn and depressed.

The Conflict Check Chart showed that she had an intense fear of deafness, ever since her mother had "lost her hearing at an early age." She was also afraid that she would die very soon, since her father had died at 50 and one of her two brothers had also died at an early age.

With Guided Association, she relived these times of fear and grief, until they no longer troubled her acutely. When she reached the stage of boredom, her symptoms began to disappear. She was much less anxious and afraid. Soon she became very well versed in Relaxation Control and combined this with the affirmation that *every day, in ever way, I am feeling better and better, stronger and stronger, younger and younger, and am hearing better and better.* She began to listen, and since she *expected* to hear better, she did, in fact, actually hear better. She was simply paying attention instead of letting the world of sound slip away from her. Within six months of this therapy, entirely in her own home, practicing each day, she was free from fear and from her symptoms. Her personality became more outgoing, and she made many more friends.

Dizziness and your emotions

This symptom may be due to many different conditions, and is sometimes part of the picture of an inner ear problem. There is sometimes nausea and vomiting with the dizziness, and some degree of deafness. In addition to the medical or surgical treatment advised by your doctors, psychosomatic therapy may be very helpful.

One of my patients was a house painter, unmarried and unhappy, living a lonely life and wedded only to alcohol. He began to develop all the usual symptoms of inner ear disease. The neurologist and the ear specialist were consulted, but they did not advise surgery. I told Mr. R. about his problem and that his only hope of avoiding surgery for increasing deafness and dizziness was to learn to use the methods described in this book. He agreed and was an apt pupil. But he refused to stop drinking. His condition was kept under control for seven years, and ended abruptly when he fell from a ladder while painting a second story wall. I do not know whether this was the result of alcohol, the dizziness of his inner ear disease, or a conscious or unconscious desire to die.

Points to remember:

1. Your eye is closely related to your emotions and to sex.
2. You often see only what you want to see, consciously or unconsciously, resulting in: squinting, degrees of blindness, night blindness, eyestrain spasm, spasm of retinal blood vessels, glaucoma (hard eyeballs).
3. Psychsomatic methods can help all these conditions.
4. You often hear only what you want to hear, consciously or unconsciously, resulting in: degrees of deafness, dizziness, ringing or buzzing in your ears.
5. These are late stages of anxiety disorders and often can be helped by psychosomatic methods of treatment.

Chapter 16

HOW TO BREATHE FOR
BETTER HEALTH AND LONGER LIFE

How to use chapter 16

You are now at the concluding chapter, but your adventure in good health is only beginning. This is a book and a method of living that you will want to keep with you and use every day of your life.

Use this program to rid yourself of your present psychosomatic health-wreckers and to prevent the development of any future problems. Daily use of these methods will keep you in the best possible psychosomatic health and will restore meaning and purpose to living. Your personality will change for the better once you are released from the fears, anxieties, and mistaken ideas of your past. You will become a warmer, more outgoing, friendlier person.

When you learn to breathe properly—and you will learn exactly how in this chapter—you will find further application of the relaxation and self-affirmation methods. As you are reading this, you are taking the vital and health-giving energy and oxygen into your lungs. Proper breathing is important general therapy for all of us; it is essential for good health and long life. It is one of the important bases for good physical and mental health.

Once you learn the close relationship between your emotions and breathing, you will see how you can use your respiratory cycle to improve your health and lengthen your life. That is the first step.

You take the next step when you observe, within yourself, the way your breathing is related to general muscle and nerve tension.

Then, you will learn exactly how to breathe, the "Westernized Yoga" method. You will see how the Yogi teaches the connection between correct breathing, mental health, control of your emotions, and even your spiritual development.

Next, you will learn how to combine correct breathing, the Complete Breath, with self-affirmation.

And finally, you will become adept in the total breathing method, using the Complete Breath with both Self-affirmation and Visualization.

You must always remember that this is basic to better health for the body-mind, just as your daily use of Guided Association, Relaxation therapy, and the other methods of this book are essential to the full release and use of your inner energies. Mastery of Self is the ultimate goal, with freedom from the psychosomatic health-wreckers.

You now hold the keys to an understanding and control of psychosomatic disease. It remains only to show you the relationship between your emotions and breathing, and how to use your respiratory cycle to improve your health and lengthen your life.

First, let me review a few of the psychosomatic health-wreckers that work on and through your respiratory system. We have already described asthma at length, and you know the relationship of emotional problems to this important and distressing disease. We have related the emotions to the common cold, perhaps the most frequent of all upper respiratory tract disorders.

You know some of the respiratory system's organ language: the repressed cry, the difficulty in "catching our breath," the way "we give vent to our feelings," the "weight on our chest," the need to "get it off our chest," the "sigh" of love, the cautionary "don't breathe a word to anyone," as well as many others. These are all evidence of the recognition, even in our daily language, that the respiratory system is one of the major sounding boards of our emotions. It ranks close to the intestinal tract for its organ language, both verbally and at the Silent Level of the emotions— the level of the wheeze, the shortness of breath, the rapid breathing of anxiety, the sharp intake of air in sudden fear, the tight chest and pain of acute or chronic worry.

Some doctors believe that *effort syndrome*—the anxious heart —is as much a respiratory problem as a cardiac disorder. Of course, it is both cardiac and respiratory, both systems being influenced by impulses bombarding them through the autonomic nervous system, fired by the chronic or acute anxiety of past and present emotional problems.

How close is the kinship of the sigh of love and the sigh of anxiety? They are one and the same, for love is always a time of deep and constant anxiety. When we are suffocated by a burden of stress, we cannot get enough air. It is a vital function that is being threatened, and the organ speaks up for its life, the life of the entire organism. The "nervous" patient often says he "cannot get enough air."

One of my most unhappy patients, a high-ranking executive with a very important industry in New York, was constantly sighing, unconscious of this sign of anxiety. He was discouraged by his son's behaviour, and the boy gave him ample reason for his anxiety. He had stolen a car and was probably a heroin addict. His father was carrying a "heavy load," as he himself put it, and his frequent sighing respiration was evidence that his lungs were aware of the weight of this "load."

He had many other evidences of psychosomatic disturbances, and most especially, frequent and severe headaches. When we spoke of key words at the time he completed his Conflict Check Chart, he suggested that the burden of his son's behaviour was his greatest "headache," and a "heavy load." He had been an over-indulgent parent, giving his son everything he wished except his love. He was always too busy making money, and saw his mistake only when it was too late.

Guided Association sessions released him from this burden of guilt, and he could then face the problem with greater understanding. His headaches became much less severe, but he then began to develop a lower back pain. I pointed out that he was simply substituting one symptom for another, and that both were obviously the result of carrying a "heavy burden." There was instant release from his backache when he recognized the truth of this observation. Relaxation therapy and practice in self-affirmation helped him control muscle spasm, both in the brain and the back.

Nevertheless, he still felt anxious and depressed, as well he might with his basic problem (his son) still unsolved. I showed him how to use the Complete Breath with self-affirmation therapy, so that he would place a firmer foundation under his general health. This had a remarkable effect, and his anxiety lessened while his general sense of well-being improved. As you will soon see, this method applies what you have already learned about self-affirmation in such fashion that it becomes as natural as breathing, and it can be put to use every moment of your day.

Breathing and muscle tension

Fear, anxiety, worry, stress of any kind are all associated with muscle tension. You already know this, and you are now informed on how to control such muscle tension (Chapter 5). And you now know that stress also changes our patterns of breathing. There are two sets of muscles intimately connected with breathing. One set is the intercostal muscle group, the muscles between the ribs. The other set is the diaphragm, the large and powerful sheet of muscle separating the lungs from the abdomen and its intestines below. And then, there are the abdominal muscles themselves, also connected with our breathing. All of these muscles are under our control, although we cannot stop breathing, even if we want to. We can, however, learn to relax these muscles of respiration; and when we do that, we will bring much of our underlying, current anxiety under control at the same time.

During your practice of the muscle relaxing methods, you noticed that your breathing became quiet, slow and controlled. This was almost automatic as your general body muscles relaxed. You cannot go into the deepest state of relaxation, nor can you fall asleep, unless your breathing is quiet and peaceful. Notice the adjective, *peaceful*, as applied to breathing. It is most important to realize that peace of mind is associated with relaxed breathing.

You will now learn something about the Yoga methods of breath control. The ancient students of human mind-body control, seeking deep inner peace in meditation and the other methods of the science of Yoga, discovered many important facts about the control of breathing. They discovered the importance of this control in quieting the mind. Indeed, they learned how to bring the respiratory cycle to such a controlled state, that it appears to be suspended altogether, almost a hibernation condition. You need not go this far in the control of your breathing, since our only concern here is with the elimination of your psychosomatic health-wreckers.

The Hindu science of breathing

The student of Yoga believes, as we all do, that breathing is essential to life. But he goes beyond our ideas of oxygen and believes that there is a vital substance in the air called *prana*, a substance that is breathed in with each breath and then can be controlled as it spreads through our nervous system. I do not ask you to accept the idea of this vital prana. It is enough to realize that there is a life-giving energy in oxygen, and we cannot live without it.

The Yogi believes that freedom from disease and normal health depend upon correct methods of breathing. He believes that he can control resistance and lengthen his life by Yoga methods of breathing. We can certainly all accept the fact that without adequate oxygen life is impossible. We also know that we must give the heart patient an increased content of oxygen in the air he breathes, and we use an oxygen tent to do this. We also use oxygen in large amounts under increased pressure for certain types of surgery, especially heart surgery, and for the treatment of otherwise fatal gas gangrene infection. And so, to this extent, we can accept the Yoga idea of the vital need for correct breathing in maintaining normal health, treating disease, and prolonging life.

And finally, the Yoga teaching is that correct breathing is essential for mental health, happiness, control of our emotions, and even for spiritual development. We can now accept the relationship between our breathing and our emotions, happiness, and mental health. We can go even further and accept the fact that breathing is an integral part of the psychosomatic disease problem. And when we come to this realization, we are ready to learn all that the Yoga has to teach, and to practice these ancient teachings brought up to date by Western science.

Nostril breathing versus mouth breathing

Yoga breathing is through the nose and not through the mouth. Modern medicine teaches the importance of breathing through the nose. The air is warmed and filtered as it passes through the nose. We should always breathe in through the nostrils and out through the mouth according to the teaching of Western medicine. This is also the teaching of Yoga, except for those special methods that call for breathing in and out through the nostrils.

Four yoga breathing methods

The most important Yoga technique may be called "Complete Breathing." Then there is High Breathing, Mid-Breathing, and Low Breathing.

High Breathing. In High Breathing the collar bones (clavicles) play an important part. In High Breathing the upper part of the lungs, the smallest part, is expanded. Relatively little oxygen gets into the lungs, by contrast with Mid-Breathing and Low Breathing. Of course, Complete Breathing brings the most oxygen into the lungs and body, for this method uses the entire lung structure.

Yoga teaches us that High Breathing is the worst type, wastes energy and gives little benefit to the body. If you want to experience High Breathing, perhaps to see how little air gets into your lungs, just stand erect and do as directed. Keep your hands at your sides. Now throw back and raise your shoulders (this raises the collar bones) and inhale. See how little air goes into your lungs, even when contrasted with your ordinary breathing. You will later be able to compare this with the fully controlled and very good Complete Breathing.

Mid-Breathing (Rib Breathing). Mid-Breathing brings the advantage of rib expansion into play and is therefore somewhat better than High Breathing. Try this by standing erect, hands at your sides as above, and breathe in while your chest expands and your abdomen is drawn in. When you pull in your abdomen, your diaphragm is pushed upward, and your lower chest expands. This is not as good as Low Breathing, and certainly less beneficial than the Yoga Complete Breathing method.

Low Breathing. This is a form of combined abdominal and diaphragm breathing. Try it by standing as above. Now let your abdominal muscles move outward as you breathe in. Follow-through, while your abdomen is still in the swelled-out position, by expanding your lower chest. You will draw in more air with this method, and the lower and mid-parts of your lungs will fill with air. Now, let your abdominal muscles tighten and draw them in, followed by tightening of your lower chest muscles. This expels the air from your lungs.

In High Breathing you fill only the upper part of your lungs. In Mid-Breathing the middle sections of the lungs are filled, and in Low Breathing the lower and middle sections are expanded. Obviously Mid-Breathing is the best of the three. But when we combine all of these, filling our entire lungs, we are practicing the best form of breathing, the Yoga Complete Breath.

Yoga Complete Breathing. This form of breathing combines the best features of the other three types. We will go beyond the usual description of this type of breathing and add the modern medical knowledge about breathing. We will then take the next step, already suggested in previous chapters, and show you how to combine this correct breathing with the all-important, self-affirmation technique. It is this combination of self-affirmation with a vital, natural function that helps produce remarkably effective relaxation and emotional release.

After you have learned to breathe correctly, using the Yoga Complete Breath, you must breathe this way all the time. This is not just for special exercise purposes, but to be used always. It will increase your chest measurements, strengthen the vital respiratory muscles, and improve the function of every part of your body. This improvement will be due partly to the increased oxygen supply and partly to the better general relaxation that results from correct breathing.

Here are your general instructions:

Stand or sit erect. You will breathe through your nostrils only. Breathe in slowly and steadily, allowing your abdomen to move outward. Your diaphragm moves down as this occurs, and your lower and middle lung areas will fill with air.

Push out your ribs and breast bone, starting from below and continuing the rib expansion upward as your lungs fill.

Continue this outward push of the ribs slowly and steadily to the upper chest region, so that the upper parts of your lungs also fill out.

Throw your shoulders slightly back, raising your collar bones (clavicles); and then, draw your lower abdomen in very slightly. This completes the first part of the breathing cycle.

You will notice that the lung expansion begins in the lower part of your lungs and gradually moves upwards to the very apices of the lungs. It is a gradual, slow, steady expansion that starts with abdominal breathing, goes on to mid- and then high breathing.

When your lungs are filled, keep them filled for the count of *seven*.

Now exhale slowly and steadily, as follows:

Gradually draw in your abdomen, letting your chest relax while your lungs empty.

Now let your chest contract from below upward, until the final motion in which your shoulders fall forward and the clavicles drop slightly downward.

The chest contraction and shoulder droop expels the last remaining air in your lungs.

Stay in this empty position for the count of *seven*.

Now repeat the cycle.

The complete breath and self-affirmation

You can learn the complete breathing method in a short time. Use it from now on. This does not mean that you must fill your lungs to the limit every time, but you should always breathe from below upward, using the abdomen, the diaphragm, the rib muscles, and the clavicles in that order. You may wish to breathe in only a moderate amount of air, and you will do it in just this way.

But you should practice full expansion deep breathing whenever you are in a relatively clean air atmosphere. In the country, away from smog and automobile exhausts, you should use this method of breathing as often as possible. It will bring pure oxygen, free from the industrial and automobile impurities of city air, into all parts of your body. The revitalizing effect cannot be overestimated.

When you do this you may gradually increase the time intervals between inspiration and expiration (breathing in and breathing out) from a count of seven to a count of fourteen or more.

As soon as the process becomes relatively automatic, you will substitute a self-affirmation for the count. While you are holding your breath, you will say:

Stronger and stronger, healthier and healthier, happier and happier, younger and younger, every day, in every way.

You will use this affirmation twice in each cycle, once after breathing in and holding your breath, and again, after breathing out and waiting for the next cycle to begin.

The continuous affirmation

As you become still more adept, you will be able to use the self-affirmation all through the breathing cycle, as well as during the rest periods. This is still more effective.

Naturally, you may use any affirmation you wish, any you may need for the particular condition under treatment. I prefer the general type above described, regardless of the psychosomatic problem. Your body knows what to do to produce the desired results, and your subconscious mind will take care of the necessary orders to your autonomic nervous system, your endocrine glands, and your other body tissues.

This method of continuous affirmation is most effective for those of us who are constantly worried, even when things are going relatively well. No one is continuously happy, but on the other hand, no one should be continuously depressed. A certain amount of anxiety is natural, but when it gets to the point that it causes a distaste for life, we are on the verge of a serious depression. This is very common and is always associated with psychosomatic symptoms in various parts of the body.

John, a bank teller, had this problem. He couldn't seem to earn enough for his family needs, and was troubled by the realization that he was getting "deeper and deeper into debt." He handled money every day, in large amounts, and still he "couldn't touch any of it" (couldn't keep it for himself). He soon began to develop a general weakness, tingling and numbness in his hands, and he was shunted from doctor to doctor as a hypochondriac. Nothing organic was ever found, despite careful studies. He became despondent and felt that he was beyond help.

His mother had died of a "heart condition," and he began to develop chest pains. His father was still alive, but had a severe and crippling arthritis, and our patient thought that his hand symptoms (numbness and tingling) meant that he was also on the way to a crippling arthritis.

The family history and the Conflict Check Chart provided important leads for Guided Association sessions, and he soon recognized the psychosomatic nature of his symptoms. He saw that he was confusing his own problems with those of his parents, and that this was a serious mistake. "After all," he finally concluded, "I am not my mother, and not my father. I have a problem, a money problem, and there is no point to taking this out on my own body." His organ language soon came under control. But his anxiety continued.

I then taught him the Complete Breath Method, with continuous affirmation. His positive statement to his subconscious mind was, "Every day, in every way, I am becoming better and better equipped to overcome my problems." These were his own words, and they were very effective. As his general health improved, he made arrangements with his own bank officers to bring his financial problem under control. Once he had faced his problem squarely, and in his familiar environment of the bank, he lost all subconscious desire to tamper with his accounts. His anxiety disappeared, and he became a "new man."

The yoga prana and self-affirmation

If you wish to use the Yoga idea of "prana," I have no objection. I would suggest that you substitute the words *life-giving energy* for *prana*, but you may use either one, as follows:

With every breath I am drawing in life-giving energy (prana) and oxygen. I am becoming younger and younger, happier and happier, healthier and healthier.

Use the deep-breathing exercise and self-affirmation just before going to sleep, perhaps while standing before an open window. I hope that you are in an atmosphere where the air is relatively clear and free from impurities. But even if you are not, you do need as much oxygen as you can get, and this is the way to get it.

If the air is very impure, you may want to buy or rent a tank of oxygen and a mask, and breathe this pure oxygen for a few breaths while practicing the self-affirmation. But do not breathe pure oxygen for too long a time, or you may become a little dizzy.

Breathing, self-affirmation, and visualization therapy

When you use self-affirmation therapy in conjunction with controlled and complete breathing, you are tying in the affirmation with your vital function of respiration. Since the affirmation must act through the unconscious mechanisms of the autonomic nervous system, under the direction of the brain's subconscious levels, the tie-in is actually between two vital and unconsciously controlled body functions. One of these two is respiration, largely out of our control under ordinary circumstances, and certainly modified greatly by our emotions, as you have seen. The other unconscious and vital function is the multiple-channelled, subconscious mechanism that regulates normal body healing during all daily living processes and in times of disease. This is also guided through the autonomic nervous system and the endocrine glands. And finally, as you have also learned, you can reach and control your autonomic nervous system through the connections in the thinking (cortical) levels of your brain, connections that reach into the thalamus and hypothalamus, and from there into the farthest reaches of the autonomic nervous system.

And that is why it is so important and valuable to use this tie-in between respiration and self-affirmation to re-channel your thinking processes, your habit patterns, your expectations, your life processes in their ultimate healing activity.

Now that you fully understand the closely integrated activity of your nervous system and the rest of your body, you can use still another body function in this vital network. This is your capacity to *visualize*, to see within your own mind. Let us assume that you have a severe headache. You may rid yourself of the head pain during your breathing and self-affirmation therapy by using the constantly repeated key word, *going, going, going, going* . . . , repeated rapidly, with gradually increasing speed (so that your mind is fully occupied with this one thought of relief), until the pain comes under control and disappears. At the same time, you will *visualize a flow of life-giving energy and oxygen* moving as a sense of warmth from your lungs, with each Yoga breath, outward to all parts of your body, but especially to your aching head.

This combination of *visualizing* the flow of healing energy from your lungs to the disturbed body area, when combined with controlled and complete respiration and self-affirmation, is most effective. I have used this method myself on many occasions over a period of 30 years, with very unusual and happy results. You can do the same. This is a completely physiological process. There is no mysticism in it. You now understand how it works at both the conscious and the unconscious levels to regulate and maintain your normal life functions. All that you are doing is taking a process that has been unconscious within your body and bringing it to the conscious, controlled level of your awareness. Once there, you have brought it under your own conscious control, and you will now use it to hasten healing and restore normal function to the distressed tissues or organ.

Until now, your negative patterns of thinking, your destructive emotional dynamite at the unconscious level, have been using these same mechanisms to lower your level of health, your resistance, your healing capacity, and actually to produce disease. Now you are reversing this unhealthy pattern of subconscious behaviour, and you are using these normal channels, these vital body mechanisms, for healing purposes.

But you must, at the same time, locate and release the repressed, emotionally unhealthy patterns imbedded in your subconscious Silent Level. You will do this by using the Conflict Check Chart and Guided Association, and you will be aided in this process by the muscle relaxation training. If you wish to combine all of these methods with a spiritual factor, bringing in the power of faith in an omnipotent God, acting within and through your own body, you may do so. Faith will indeed move mountains.*

Points to remember:

1. Breathing is closely related to your emotions.
2. Asthma, the common cold, shortness of breath, and the respira-

---

* For a complete discussion of this matter, see UNITROL. (Parker Publishing Co., 1965.) Full information is available from the UNITROL Teaching Institute, 147-41 Sanford Ave., Flushing, N.Y

tory system's organ language, all demonstrate this close emotional tie-in between breathing and your subconscious mind.

3. You must and can learn to control the breathing cycle. This gives you partial control over the emotions and psychosomatic diseases of the respiratory tract.
4. One method to accomplish this is by control of muscle tension.
5. Another control method is by learning correct breathing, the Yoga Complete Breath.
6. Still another control method is by the combined Complete Breathing–Self-Affirmation technique.
7. The most complete symptom control comes from the Breathing, Self-Affirmation, and Visualization Treatment.

This method supplements the basic Conflict Check Chart–Guided Association therapy to help you rid yourself of your psychosomatic health-wreckers.

Index

INDEX